# THE SELF-BUILD *Dream*

Jason Orme

ovolo

# THE SELF-BUILD *Dream*

**Ovolo Books**
**Manor Lodge, Grass Yard,**
**Huntingdon,**
**Cambridgeshire**
**PE28 0HQ**



**ISBN: 9781905959167**



All of the material in this book has previously appeared in Homebuilding & Renovating magazine - Britain's best selling monthly for selfbuilders and renovators (www.homebuilding.co.uk).

Design: Gill Lockhart

**This edition first published by Ovolo Books**
**April 2011**

Printed in the Czech Republic

# CONTENTS

# What is *self-build?*

If you are interested in finding the answer to this question we've created this book just for you. This is where your journey to create your own home begins. . .

When so much of the rest of our lives is so highly personalised, it seems odd that so many of us are happy to leave our homes up to other people. We spend ages choosing our cars and clothes, yet in most cases no more than half an hour looking at the home we're going to be spending years of our lives in.

There is, thankfully, another way. Self-building allows you to create a home that is built just with you in mind – so you're not compromising on room shapes and sizes or the exterior style but rather having something that fits you and your family's needs perfectly.

The problem, of course, is that it sounds difficult. But this book is here to show you that, in fact, you can build your own home without actually building it at all; you can specify exactly what you want and get the same great result with the tiniest of disruption to the rest of your lives. We'll show you what the process involves and the choices self-building opens up to you so you can see for yourself whether you'd like to try it.

We've organised the following pages into three sections, the first exploring what it's all about and hopefully helping you to decide whether it's for you. Further into the book, we go into more detail about what you can achieve and how to achieve it. It serves as a definitive introduction to the subject and I hope that it will serve to inspire you to join me, and hundreds of thousands of others, who will never be able to 'make-do' with their houses again

**JASON ORME**

***Editor, Homebuilding and Renovatiing Magazine***

# WHAT IS *Self-build?*

## Is self-build for me?

How will building your own home affect you? The impact on your life needn't be as great as you might think

### WHAT DOES IT MEAN?

There are around 20,000 self-built homes each year in the UK, but the term 'self-build' applies to many different routes all hoping to achieve the same destination: an individually designed and built home with a specific owner in mind. The term itself conjures up images of the owner literally building his own home through DIY – and while this is accurate in a small minority of self-built homes, the vast majority of self-builders have little experience or knowledge of homebuilding itself. Indeed, the overwhelming majority of self-built homes are in fact built by professional builders or companies on behalf of the eventual owner.

Catherine and Donald Bisset built their stylish five bedroom family home on a DIY basis for jus £150,000

# Is self-build for me?

Steve and Sally Gorvin built a contemporary style new home on the Dorset coast that makes the most of amazing views

The thing that unites all self-built homes is that the owner is at the centre of the process. Unlike a developer-built home – the ones you will see on housing estates up and down the land – the home is built for a specific owner, meaning that it can be tailored to meet their unique needs. That owner will already own the building plot on which the house sits, and they will have commissioned a designer to come up with a house design that is specific to them, So while in regular housing the eventual occupant is at the end of the line – a marketing afterthought, in reality – in self-build, the occupant is at the heart of the process from start to finish.

It's interesting to note at this stage the terms other countries use to describe their self-builders. 'Custom builders' tends to be the main phrase used in the United States and Australia, and it serves well to illustrate the unique, owner-specific nature of the process.

So whether you want to be involved in a hands-on building project – perhaps if you're recently retired or have experience in the industry and finally want to do something for yourself – or if you are a busy professional able only to occasionally check progress and sign off design schemes, then you too can be considered a self-builder.

## THE BENEFITS

Whichever way you approach this project, it's undoubtedly going to be harder work and more stressful than simply buying a house. There are plenty of hurdles to negotiate and potential pitfalls. So why do people go down this route when there are 1,000s of homes available to buy?

Peter and Betty Jolley's single storey Devon self-build combines practicality for their later years with their love of modernist architectural style

# *A home designed just for you*

There is always some level of compromise in a pre-made house that you buy. It might be that there aren't enough bathrooms to match the number of bedrooms; the living room might be too small, or there might not be a separate home office. It's also possible that it doesn't look like your dream home – perhaps the windows are too small, or the roof tiles don't look right, or the porch is ugly. While it's true that many of these things can be rectified through a long and expensive process of remodelling and extending, you're paying for what is in effect someone else's idea of what a home should be and look like.

*By self-building you can end up with a house that truly reflects your own specific needs and desires.*

A home on the open market might also not have any of the things that you would really love in a house – such as a spectacular double-height entrance hall, or a large breakfast kitchen area, or even simpler things like underfloor heating or folding sliding doors that open out onto a patio.

Although it would be incorrect to say that self-builders create without restriction – they work to budgets and the constraints imposed by the local planning authorities – it's

You can build homes on all sorts of sites – Sandra Metcalfe's oak frame home in Cornwall is built around a slope

fair to say that by self-building you can end up with a house that truly reflects your own specific needs and desires. So both in terms of the accommodation provided (number of bedrooms and bathrooms, shape and size of living spaces, open plan or not, and so on) and the look of the house (perhaps a particular period style, or in simpler terms the right bricks, windows, driveway, timber cladding), self-building enables you to create exactly what you want in a house.

While many smaller developers do build homes of high design standards, the conservatism of the main big-name housebuilders means that many of the new-built homes you can buy today suffer in design quality. They often simply don't look terribly attractive from the outside, with strange roof pitches, badly-detailed windows and doors, and an overall misjudged take on Georgian style. Inside, they notoriously suffer from too-small (and sometimes too many) bedrooms, a misguided loyalty to the importance of the dining room and modest-sized kitchens. Not to mention that you rarely come across features that are now standard in self-built homes, such as underfloor heating and renewable energy. The developer's only interest, of course, is maximising the marketable value of the property – as any self-builder will recognise, this

*In developer-built homes you rarely come across features that are now standard in self-builds.*

Self-builders can utilise all sorts of different techniques. Kevin and Rose McCabe built their own home out of cob – mud mixed with straw and aggregates

Self-building gives you the chance to live in a period style home that is energy efficient enough to keep running costs low, as Jeremy Taylor found

doesn't always make for a house that is great to live in.

Of course, many people like to buy 'second-hand' homes and often, quite rightly, associate them with character and in-built charm – particularly those built before the 1930s. For many people old cottages or grand Georgian country homes are quintessentially British and living in them hugely evocative. Self-builders can enjoy living in an 'old' home too, however – one complete with all the design charm and, if well-finished, instant character. New 'old' houses are a significant part of the self-build world, with companies specialising in recreating mediaeval oak-framing and designers renowned for their success in replicating Georgian and cottage styles. And, of course, your new 'old' house won't suffer from the horrific heating bills that the genuine article will.

So whatever your dream home – strikingly modern or a total throwback, with a home cinema, huge family kitchen and master bedroom suite complete with dressing room, perhaps – self-building really is the only way to get it.

*New 'old' houses are a significant part of the self-build world, with companies specialising in recreating mediaeval oak-framing*

**Not as grand as a Georgian mansion but still with masses of character and totally unique**

# A home that performs

More than ever, we are aware of build quality in our homes. Self-building is a way to create a home that doesn't just look how you want it to, but also performs how you would expect.

While many existing homes on the market – particularly those built by high-end developers – are now built to a high quality, the vast majority of existing homes fall well short in terms of their build standards; the majority of new-build homes do nothing more than meet basic building regulations requirements.

*The market is the only thing that matters to the developer, the inclination is to minimise capital cost and do the bare minimum for the maximum return*

The result of living in a home that hasn't been built to a high standard probably won't be apparent when you're looking around it to buy, or even in the first few weeks after moving in. But it will slowly become apparent – most notably in wafer-thin partition walls that mean you can hear every noise clearly throughout the house; in the cheap kitchen units that slam shut; in the draughts around doors and windows; in the showers that effect nothing more than a weak mist; and, above all, the first few energy bills.

Again, because the market is the only thing that matters to the developer, the inclination is to minimise capital cost and do the bare minimum for the maximum return. There is, of course, absolutely

CASE STUDY

SUPER INSULATED ECO-FRIENDLY TIMBER-FRAME HOUSE

**Monique and Laurence Steijger's super-insulated new eco-friendly timber frame house cost less than £200,000 to build and requires no central heating**

no encouragement to install features that only pay off in the long term, as the concept of repeat business is alien to the housing market.

Older homes, of course, suffer worse because they weren't even subject to the most basic of building regulations. So while a building surveyor might put you off buying a house because of structural problems, issues of what self-builders would consider poor quality are standard on many old homes. The most obvious, of course, are draughts and a lack of insulation in the walls causing huge heating bills.

Self-builders, however, can prioritise build quality. Because they are going to be living in the house after it is built, they can ensure that extra insulation is added, and that airtightness tests are carried out; that block-built partition walls are included upstairs to minimise sound travel, and that windows are perhaps triple glazed to reduce heat loss. They can install heat pumps and solar panels safe in the knowledge that, while they might not add a huge amount to the end value of the house initially, they as owner will benefit from tiny heating bills for the next 20 years. They can specify solid plastered walls rather than using plasterboard to get that solid feel; real plaster mouldings rather than polystyrene alternatives; in-built storage into bedrooms; underfloor heating; mechanical ventilation with filters to reduce pollen in the house; low-energy lights to reduce electricity bills. The list is endless, but the truth is simple – self-built homes perform better than any other.

*Self-builders can ensure that extra insulation is added, airtightness tests are carried out; and that windows are perhaps triple glazed to reduce heat loss*

## "The house is so energy efficient is doesn't need a conventional central heating system

**MONIQUE AND LAURENCE STEIJGER built their own home in Derbyshire because they couldn't find what they wanted on the property market. It's no wonder, because their requirements were pretty exacting – a home that would be so energy efficient it wouldn't need a conventional central heating system.**

**Making the most of large amounts of insulation, renewable energy and the heat gained from lots of south-facing glazing – as well as plenty of recycled materials – their new home is surely the last word in sustainability**

# Is self-build for me?

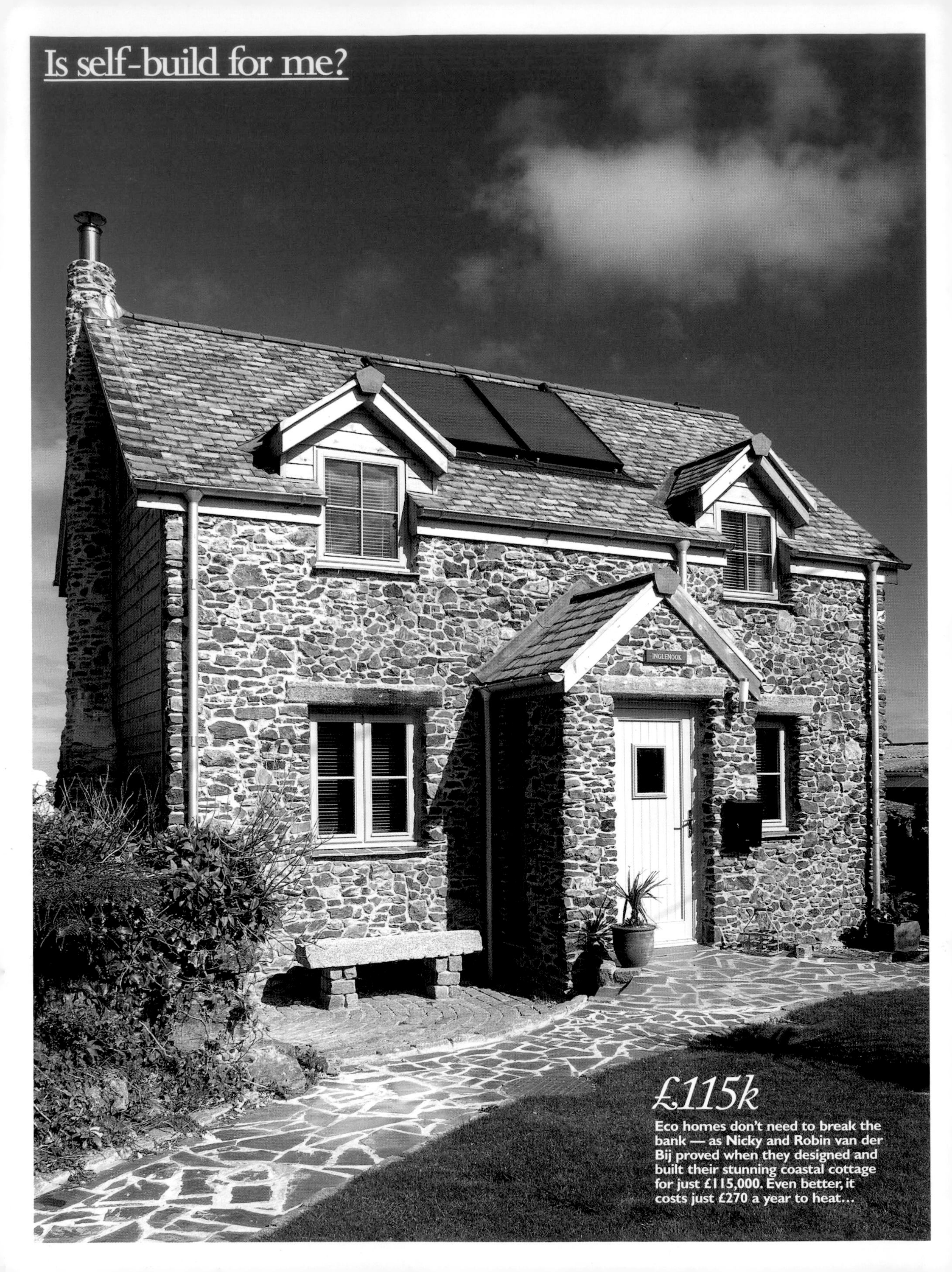


## £115k

**Eco homes don't need to break the bank — as Nicky and Robin van der Bij proved when they designed and built their stunning coastal cottage for just £115,000. Even better, it costs just £270 a year to heat…**

# VALUE FOR MONEY
## *A new home at cost price*

When you buy a new home off a developer, part of the purchase price is the profit that the developer quite rightly enjoys off the venture. In most cases, depending on the local market, this is between 10-30% of the end value. Likewise, the price of an existing older house is likely to be inflated somewhat by comparison to the price of local new-built homes.

By self-building, and effectively taking on the role of the developer, you are saving that 10-30% off the purchase price and basically buying a new home at cost price.

As a result, many self-builders are motivated not just by design and quality issues but also by saving huge amounts of money on the value of their house – a great way to create instant equity. Indeed, many self-builders enjoy this part of the process so much that they self-build two, three or even more times over the course of their lives, primarily to build their way up the property ladder. So couples who might struggle to be able to afford a home in a nice area can do so by self-building; families who want a bigger home in their surrounding area but can't afford to make the step up, say, from semi- to detached home, can afford to do so by self-building; likewise, people who want to quickly build their way up the property ladder might self-build three times in ten years, using the equity they have created to either reduce their mortgage or afford a bigger, grander home than they could have ever dreamt of affording.

*£80k* This home in Wiltshire was self-built by two teachers for just £80,000

*£59k* This house in Scotland cost the owner just £59,000 to build

*£125k* Self-building helped the owners of this Oxfordshire home to stay in the village

**TIP** In flat housing markets, self-build (and, to a lesser extent, renovation and extension) is the only way to create equity apart from reducing your mortgage.

Eco homes should be built out of sustainable materials such as oak

Self-building enables you to incorporate features to help reduce running bills, such as this green roof

## ENERGY EFFICIENCY

Put simply, self-building is the easiest and best way to live in a house that is cheap to run and even completely self-sufficient. If you're worried about rising future energy costs, or even the stability of future supplies, then by self-building you can create a home that not only minimises the amount of energy it actually needs (through extra insulation, low-energy lighting, passive solar gain and more) but can produce that energy on site, independently of the grid. Renewable features like solar panels, wind turbines, heat pumps and the like work best when fitted together, and into a house that is designed with those features in mind.

CASE STUDY

LOW-ENERGY FARMHOUSE

> We wanted to build a low-energy house that would be visually exciting

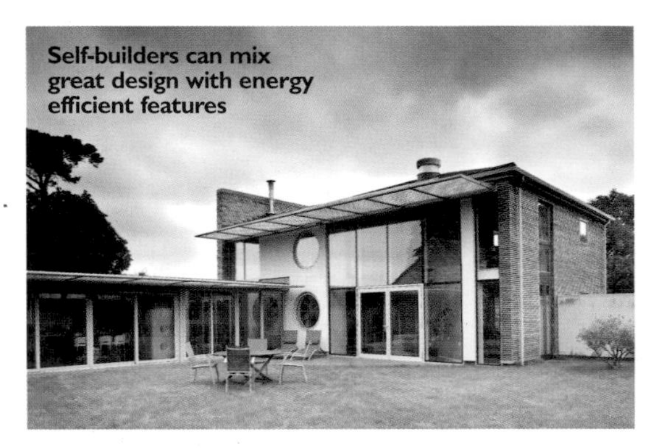
Self-builders can mix great design with energy efficient features

**RICHARD AND SIAN LIWICKI'S LOW-ENERGY, contemporary-style farmhouse in Oxfordshire is a true blend of energy efficiency and design style. "We wanted to build a low-energy house that would be visually exciting and would make the most of the wonderful views," explains Richard. The resulting home, which incorporates solar panels to generate both hot water and electricity, is designed to draw in the heat from the sun during the spring, autumn and winter with shading above the glass to keep it cooler in summer.**

The heart of this house is a central double-height space that provides heat for the other rooms

The Morgans built their delightful oak-framed cottage for £134,000

# *Who Self-builds?*

Self-build really is something that anyone can do, providing that they can fund the equivalent of a house purchase. While the majority of self-builders tend to realise their dream after owning regular houses for many years, some people self-built to create their first home together; others self-build to create a home perfect for their retirement. There are several common groups:

## FIRST-TIME BUYERS

Unable to afford to make the first rung on their local housing ladder, a young couple might turn to self-building in order to get their first home together. Money is likely to be very tight and so this couple might look for a gift of a building plot from parents or perhaps to grab a bargain plot that might be someone's side garden. They will build a small but sufficient home – possibly one of them has experience in the building industry or can keep costs down by using friends in the know - for their needs and look to move on in a few years' time, enjoying a big helping hand up the housing ladder.

Self-building is a perfect way for young families to create a bigger home without paying full market value

## YOUNG FAMILY

An early thirtysomething couple will probably be looking for a bigger house to meet the need for more accommodation for their growing family. The step up from semi-detached or terraced home to something more significant is often excessive, and so they might look to buy a building plot and build a modest-sized detached home in order to get the space they need, in the area they want, at the right price.

## FORTYSOMETHINGS

With more income and freedom, a fortysomething family might self-build because they want to create their dream home – with a home cinema, bedroom suites for teenage children and an annexe for elderly parents. They are likely to be more motivated by the design of their house and feel frustrated at what they have found on the regular market.

Many retired couples like to create something architecturally interesting

# Is self-build for me?

John and Dulcie Blain built a contemporary style home in an old quarry

A perfect low-energy home by the sea

A contemporary home much bigger than this couple could have otherwise afforded

## RETIREES

With minimal or no mortgage and children no longer living at home, a recently retired couple has the freedom to create a home that will meet their changing needs and desire for low running costs – all with an eye on the budget. They might also want to create a legacy, with an exciting individual design.

## DIY ENTHUSIASTS OF ALL AGES

Building your own home is the ultimate DIY project and many people dream of one day spending their time literally building their new house. This is likely to appeal to recent retirees or those who have worked in the building industry and are finally able to spend time on their own ventures.

NEWCOMERS

### BUT I REALLY DO KNOW NOTHING ABOUT BUILDING!

**As a complete newcomer it's easy to be put off from self-building – it can be a world of mysterious terminology and seemingly overwhelming technical complexity. Don't worry – the truth is that many self-builders don't ever know what many of the terms mean, and enjoy the learning process that a project like this gives them. It's only really important that you surround yourself with experts (designer, builder) who know what they're talking about and can advise you about the choices you face. We've also included an A-Z of terms at the back of this book!**

CASE STUDY

DIY SELF-BUILD

# I'm so proud, it's an extraordinatary thing to do for someone who's never built a house before....

**"IT HAD EVERYTHING** we wanted and was so pretty," says Catherine Bisset of the riverside plot which she and husband Donald purchased for £162,000. The couple previously lived in a two bedroom terrace, but struggled to find a new home for their growing family at the right price — until they hit upon the idea of self-build. Donald put his job as an oil-rig inspector on hold to take on project management and much of the work, including digging the foundations, roofing, plumbing and constructing the timber frame — the latter saved the couple £12,000. "I'm so proud of what he's achieved. It's an extraordinary thing for someone who's never built a house before," smiles Catherine. A tight control of costs meant they kept to the £150,000 budget.

A DIY project isn't for everybody – it took Donald nine months to build after taking a career break

Self-building provided the perfect chance for this young family to get a bigger, better home in the right place

> "Friends had bought the site and were selling it off as serviced plots – we were in the right place at the right time

The house is so well insulated that the Paton's have been turning off the underfloor heating – even in winter

**NEIL AND LYNDA PATON** have self-built an award-winning eco home - yet the couple didn't originally intend to set out on the self-build route. Instead, they started off looking for existing local properties to buy. "We were looking for a house but didn't see anything that we liked," says Lynda. "I don't know what the future holds, but for the time being this house suits are needs perfectly. Having previously lived in a house where we had rooms we'd only use on occasion, it's good to be in a home where every space is utilised. And because of the insulation we don't continually have to shut doors to keep the heat in"

Neil and Lynda's new home has been constructed using a post and beam frame made from Douglas fir. Externally it has been clad in untreated larch, whilst the slate roof features solar panels

CASE STUDY

OAK FRAME SELF-BUILD

> Jan and Mike completed the floor themselves. They laid their own underfloor heating too.

**THERE ARE THOSE PEOPLE** who approach their impending retirement with the gleeful intent to have a very long, well-earned rest — quite understandable given the decades spent slogging away in the workplace. But then there is that other type of person who can't resist the opportunity to do something a little bit special – albeit challenging – with that extra time. Two such people are Jan and Mike Davies, who together have built a beautiful oak framed cottage – clad in brick and infilled with energy-efficient SIPs (structural insulated panels) – carrying out a large amount of work on a DIY basis. It cost £270,000 to build.

Although oak-framed the cottage is clad in brick to match neighbouring properties. It's built on part of their former garden

# To: Kildare Naas

# Intransit Item

Branch: Kildare Celbridge
Date: 7/10/2022 Time: 1:05 PM

Item: The self-build dream: how to build your own home
A973174

rom: Kildare Celbridge
o: Kildare Naas

nstruction: Please process item

# WHAT IS SELF-BUILD?

PART ONE

One of the main hurdles to self-building is finding a plot – so much so that many self-builders resort to knocking down older properties that have fallen into poor condition

# *The Negatives*

If all of this was easy, of course, everyone would build their own homes. It's important to be aware of the potential pitfalls and problems that any self-build project can face.

## IT'S DIFFICULT TO FIND A PLOT

The number one thing that stops many would-be self-builders before they even start is the failure to find a suitable building plot. Self-builders face stiff competition from professional builders, developers and, of course, other self-builders for the relatively few plots that come up in each location each year – at the right price. A bit like looking for the perfect house, the main reason for failure is that they're looking for something they are never going to find. There is a distinct lack of suitable building plots – usually linked to 'hot' local housing markets – but it's usually possible to get around this by applying some plotfinding tips (see page 68).

## RAISING THE MONEY

If you can afford to buy a house, then you can afford to self-build – but borrowing money from banks and building societies to build your own home isn't quite as easy as getting a regular mortgage. Whilst lending criteria are based on the same principles that apply to regular house mortgages, many lenders require quite healthy deposits – currently around 15-20% of the cost of the plot, and the same for the build cost itself. Most people sell their existing property and move into rented accommodation to release the money to cover this.

## WHERE WILL I LIVE WHILST I BUILD?

Contrary to popular myth, you really don't need to live in a caravan while your new home gets built – although it does massively help in cutting costs. Most families opt to sell their existing home and rent or live with family for the period of construction (usually around 12 months). In order to be in a great position to buy a building plot without having to wait to sell their own house, most self-builders sell their own house before even thinking about buying a plot.

It is however possible, providing you can afford it, to fund two mortgages at the same time. In many cases an individual's primary lender/bank is the starting point, although specialist self-build mortgage providers will also be able to help.

*Contrary to popular myth, you really don't need to live in a caravan while your new home gets built – although it does massively help in cutting costs.*

## A STRESSFUL EXERCISE

Whilst the overwhelming majority of self-build projects experience a major stress-test at some stage, watching TV programmes of people building their own home does tend to over-egg the levels of stress. There's no question that this is a major life experience. The fact that a building site – one likely to have a huge proportion of your wealth tied up on it, too – is well outside most people's comfort zone is in itself pretty stressful. Combine that with the occasional bust-up with a builder, or a late-running supplier, and the whole thing can be an assault on the nerves.

Most of the stress-instigators are based on the issues of meeting tight budgets and deadlines. It is possible to reduce these stresses through good planning and forethought – a proper estimation of costs, for example – and by coming into the project with a fairly relaxed attitude. If you think stress might be an issue for you, however, you are probably best to engage with a specialist design and build package company – meaning pretty much guaranteed costs, no site visits for you and a less intense, if slightly less satisfying, experience.

## 'COWBOY BUILDERS' & ON-SITE DISPUTES

Listen to the mainstream media and you'll believe that the number one problem any self-builder faces is so-called 'cowboy' builders. In reality, as with any profession, there are a few bad apples but the overwhelming majority of builders are honest, hardworking and simply trying to earn a fair living. Avoiding the bad ones is actually pretty easy (see page xx) and certainly not something that should put anyone off.

That said, a fair number of self-build projects do experience some sort of difficulty between client (you) and builder (or subcontractor, such as a plasterer or plumber). Avoiding disputes is very difficult but the main reasons they happen is usually down to poor communication – perhaps a misinterpretation of plans, or wrongly assuming that someone else was taking care of a delivery, or more likely that you weren't expecting a particular invoice. The key, especially when it comes to payment, is to be clear and upfront about what you'll be paying and when. It's also worth noting that, unlike many projects, building can be an occasionally messy and confused job. Pragmatism can go a long way, although you do need to stand up for what you want.

*In reality, as with any profession, there are a few bad apples but the overwhelming majority of builders are honest, hardworking and simply trying to earn a fair living.*

## OVER BUDGET, AND OVER SCHEDULE

The main fear for self-builders is being responsible for a project that seems to spiral out of all control – costing much more than they estimated and seemingly months off its intended completion date. The self-builder is left pumping what remains of their life savings into a project they now despise and there's little on the horizon to imagine the house being finished.

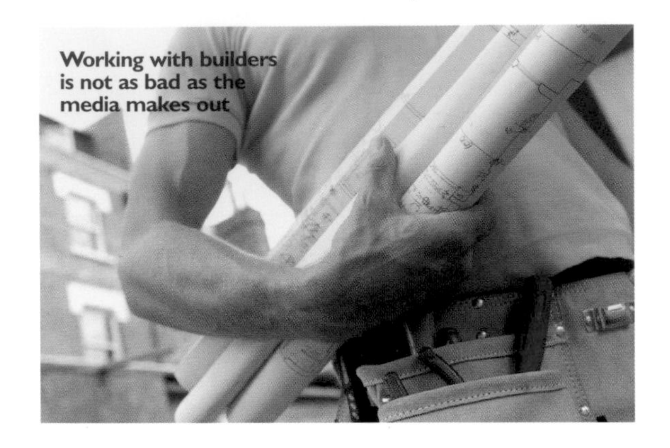
Working with builders is not as bad as the media makes out

A typical house build takes between 9-12 months

While things can go wrong on site, these situations usually occur because of poor planning and poor design, rather than incidental mistakes. When faced with the issue of a spiralling budget, most experts would say that the project was starting off on the wrong track and the initial budget was completely unrealistic. Either that, or the self-builder changed their mind significantly during the build.

It's critical to ensure that the design you go ahead and build is based realistically on your building budget. This is a skill that some designers do not possess – you need to make sure that your designer has it. Likewise, you need to make sure that the drawings you send out to get builders to quote on is as accurate and complete as possible – too many grey areas and the price they give you becomes more of a guessing game. There is absolutely no reason why a complete and accurate 'specification' (the detailed list of what's going into the house) and drawings should not result in a house completed to the expected cost and timeframe.

*It's critical to ensure that the design you go ahead and build is based realistically on your building budget. This is a skill that some designers do not possess.*

Many self-builders do in fact keep some money back as a 'contingency' (usually around 10% of the total budget) for the little things that are impossible to predict on site. It's a wise idea as building can be an unpredictable business.

SELF-BUILD IN THE UK

## AN INTERNATIONAL CONTEXT

**Despite its growing popularity, the UK lags well behind most other countries when it comes to the amount of self-built homes it produces. In Australia, for instance, most developers sell individual building plots (blocks) on pre-drawn estates in the same way that developers over here sell homes on estates. In Germany and throughout the rest of Europe, self-building is much more mainstream too. The main reason it's different is that the planning system over here is much stricter.**

# PART TWO

# WHAT'S INVOLVED IN *Self-building?*

## The Build Process

## *The Different Ways to Self-build*

It's possible to find a way of achieving your goal of an individual home in many different ways to suit your own situation and wishes. Indeed, one of the keys to a successful project of this sort is to find the right route for your specific skills and resources.

## COMPLETELY HANDS-OFF

If you're either unwilling or unable to get too involved in the day-to-day processes, then you can be a self-builder – with the emphasis on minimising the 'self'. Specialist design and build 'package' companies will be able to provide you with a design and organise a team of builders, reporting to them, to manage the build for you – you can have as little or as much say as you want in the details. At the extreme end, your involvement can literally amount to signing off an agreed design and being given the keys to your finished home months down the line. If you prefer, you'll never have to talk once to a builder. This is sometimes called a 'Turnkey' approach, simply describing the client's involvement. Can't find a plot? Well, many package companies also offering plotfinding services (or you can simply choose from their list of plots in your area.)

**PROS:**
- **Minimises stress;**
- **Usually get a fixed price for the job, reducing risk;**

**CONS:**
- **Most expensive way to self-build;**
- **Difficult to retain control over details;**
- **Reduced feeling of involvement & attachment**

## ARCHITECT/BUILDER

The majority of self-builders use this route. The self-builder will find their plot, and then find and engage with a house designer (who may or may not be an Architect) to come up with an agreed house design. With the designer's help, a builder will be found who will then manage the building project itself, bringing in the majority of their own materials and using their own network of local plumbers, electricians and so on to complete the project. The builder may either deal with the supervising designer (who will check the project is being built to the agreed design) or with the self-builder directly, depending on the arrangement. It's worth noting here that a builder in this role might also be referred to as a main contractor – meaning simply that they are responsible for the contract and bringing in their own 'sub' contractors.

This route minimises the amount of direct involvement the novice self-builder may have with the

CASE STUDY

LOW-ENERGY FARMHOUSE

**ARCHITECHT/BUILDER**

# Using a builder freed our time

**Stuart and Pat Smith are busy people, running their own IT company, and so when it came to the construction of their new home on a spectacular site in Devon, they opted to be fairly hands-off. They collaborated with architect Lee Guilfoyle on the design while, for the construction, builder Peter Passmore rose to the challenge, and was duly crowned 'Master Builder of the Year' by the Federation of Master Builders (FMB) for his efforts. "It wasn't a straightforward job, but we broke it up into stages and it all came together," Peter says. "This is our biggest project to date and the most interesting and challenging. The Smiths were great, and we have become firm friends." He turned out to be the fantasy builder everyone dreams of finding: personally attending the site on a daily basis, co-ordinating deliveries along the awkward, narrow access road, and accommodating Pat and Stuart's many last-minute changes without batting an eyelid. Even the subcontractors' meal breaks were carefully timed with the aid of a bell.**

The house makes the most of its location with stunning panoramic views from the dining area

Two forward-facing wings ensure that the views may be enjoyed from virtually every room. The sloping site has been sculpted and landscaped to create wind-break terraces, decks and water features

building process but enables them to have involvement at the key stages along with some exposure to the building process. The use of a designer/Architect to supervise the build project is very much the traditional self-build approach, and is slowly fading owing in part to the increased use of structural warranty inspections.

One interesting twist on this route is the increased use of independent 'project managers' – usually either experienced/semi-retired builders or, in fact, been-there-done-that self-builders who feel they can make a living organising other peoples' projects. They will offer a service that organises the project on your behalf – cutting out the role of the main contractor and directly hiring contractors such as groundworkers, bricklayers, roofers and so on, in addition to organising the delivery of materials.

**PROS:**

- **Best way for busy people to feel involved in the process**
- **Enables greater control and decisions over details**
- **Having an architect on your side gives greater protection**

**CONS:**

- **Important to choose the right designer and builder**
- **Relatively expensive – the builder will take a profit**
- **Difficult to keep a lid on costs**

## MANAGING THE PROJECT

This approach uses a designer/architect to come up with an agreed house design on a plot you own. The self-builder will take on the role of the main contractor/builder/project manager, organising everything from the delivery of all the materials to the lining up of all the individual tradesmen. The commitment is very much centered around visiting site at least twice a day – in the morning to take delivery of materials and in the evening to check work and tidy the site – but also involves plenty of phoning around, lining up the tradesmen and keeping on top of the schedule. Additionally, as project manager, the self-builder will be responsible for arranging the regular site inspections along with assorted site management issues.

**PROS:**

*continued on page 40*

CASE STUDY

SELF-MANAGED BUILD

**MANAGING THE PROJECT**

## Delivered under budget

**CARON PAIN'S SELF-BUILD STORY IS quite simply inspirational. She built a large, well-appointed house in Norfolk in double-quick time and at an amazingly keen price by managing the project herself – despite holding down a job as a teaching assistant and being a busy mum. In fact, her cost control has been so good that she managed to come in £20,000 under her £130,000 budget. In doing so, she has built up a huge increase in the equity of her house. Not only that, but the house took just six months from start to finish. Caron bought all of her own materials and managed a team of tradesmen on site every day.**

**The house is a great example of the fact that you can build a basic but comfortable home in a very cost-effective way. It also demonstrates that if you need or want to get involved in managing or carrying out the build then there are considerable savings to be made.**

The whole house cost Caon just £130,000 and is an inspiractional example of what can be achieved through sel-build

• For those without DIY skills, it's the closest way to get involved
• Save money – no builder's mark-up on materials or labour
• Plenty of control over details

**CONS:**

• Stressful, particularly if you have other commitments
• Requires some understanding of build schedules
• Requires a good local network of tradesmen

## DIY

As simple as it sounds, it is possible but not easy to build a home using just your own labour. You can, if you wish, also design it yourself. The DIY self-builder will not only physically lay every block and brick, fix the roof structure and lay tiles, do all the plastering, plumbing and electrics – not to mention the foundations, floor structures, joinery, finishing and landscaping – but will also have to co-ordinate the delivery of materials and additional help when required either from friends or the certified professionals required to complete certain tasks (such as electrics). The commitment is obviously huge both in terms of effort and time, but the rewards are great, both financially (traditionally labour accounts for around 50% of the cost of any homebuilding project, so there are huge savings to be made) and in terms of the feeling of achievement. Don't forget that regular inspections by the local Building Inspector and Warranty Inspector will ensure that any work you do meets set standards.

**PROS:**

• Save £10,000s off the price of a regular self-build – DIY is the only way you can realistically build a house for next to nothing
• Huge feeling of involvement and achievement
• The best way to get attached to your house and understand how it works
• Achieve true control over what's done, and how

**CONS:**

• Massively time consuming – most DIY self-builds take years
• Whilst not always skilful, most tasks are physically demanding
• It's not just DIY – you also need plenty of time to organise the site

CASE STUDY

RETIREMENT PROJECT

**DO IT YOURSELF**

# Impressive achievement

**JOHN AND JILL PRICE SPENT the best part of four years building their own home but the results are outstanding – a stylish barn-style home that cost them less than a quarter of its value to complete. John wanted to build his own home as a retirement project and despite having minimal DIY experience thoroughly enjoyed the self-build. "The fact of the matter is that with some practical ability, some building experience, and a lot of time and patience, it is possible to achieve quite a lot. I had some help with the heavy work, too, which helped immensely," says John. The project took a bit longer than John had hoped — clocking in at a little over four years with a small gap along the way. "He didn't tell me it would take quite this long," says Jill with a smile, happy to have seen John accomplish something so impressive (she was responsible for much of the interior specification).**

The home cost just a quarter of its current value to build over a four-year period

As well as being financially worthwhile John enjoyed the build

# The build process

# How Long Will it All Take?

When you think about the process of building your own home, it's best to think about it in two separate parts. Firstly, there is the pre-build element, and secondly, the actual construction.

## THE PRE-BUILD PROCESS

It is impossible to put a timeline on the first part of your self-build journey – finding a plot. Imagine buying a house, only with many less houses and much more interest. It could take a matter of weeks; you might even own the plot already (i.e. it's your garden, or you're going to knock your own house down and rebuild it); more likely it might take several months. If it begins to take longer than that, then you're probably looking for the wrong thing.

Once you've found a plot, our timeline begins.

**DESIGN:** 1-3 months First of all you'll need to get a working design for it which by the time you've found a suitable designer and been through the design consultation, will take between one and three months. You'll then apply for planning permission.

**PLANNING PERMISSION:** 2-3 months: Assuming that the planning authorities approve your scheme (the designer may well have consulted with them during the design process) you should get an answer back within 8 weeks.

*Some timber frame package companies claim to be able to get a house ready and liveable within six months. Many DIY self-builders take upwards of three years.*

**FINDING A BUILDER:** You can be lining up builders during the design and planning processes, but you won't get a realistic price or availability until you've got planning permission. In theory you can wait months for a suitable builder, but if you've done your research, you should be able to get one ready to start within a few months of gaining planning approval. If you're dealing with a package company (particularly one that provides a timber frame kit) then your wait before starting work on site will depend on how busy their order book is. In some cases you could wait around six months for delivery. Obviously if you're going down a DIY route, then you can get started the minute you've got conditional building regulations approval.

**BUILDING REGULATIONS APPROVAL:** Once you've got planning permission and agreed a specification you can apply for conditional approval from your local Building Control department on your plans. This will usually take 2-4 weeks.

So in total, assuming things pass relatively as planned, you will expect to own a plot for between six and twelve months before work commences.

## THE HOUSE CONSTRUCTION

For many people the start of work on site is a huge boost after months waiting around for something to happen. It is, in many ways, the beginning of the end of your self-build journey. The construction process is broken down into two distinct elements – pre and post weathertight stage (this is also called 'getting a house to shell'). A house is deemed to be 'weathertight' (sometimes also called 'watertight') when the walls are up, the roof is on, the windows and doors are in and it's all fully lockable – and, from the outside, resembles a finished house.

Getting a house to weathertight is easily the most exhilarating part of the process for beginners – it's when all the heavy work is done, and real progress can be seen almost every day. Depending on its size, most builders would expect to get a house to weathertight in three to six months.

It usually takes between 30-45% of the complete construction process.

Once a house is weathertight, work can commence inside. Owing to the complexities of houses, there is a complex schedule that needs to be followed – the plasterers can't work at the same time as the initial electrics are being done, for instance – which tends to mean that it's this element of the process that can drag on a bit. A weathertight house can be made liveable in between four and twelve months, depending on its size and complexity and, of course, how efficient the schedule is.

So, in total, expect a house to go from 'breaking ground' (the traditional start of a project) to moving in in between eight and twelve months.

# PACKAGE COMPANIES
## *The ideal solution for beginners*

For someone who's new to the idea of building their own home, it can seem pretty daunting. There's a lot of potential pitfalls and thanks to the mainstream media, horror stories about dealing with builders and suppliers add to the fears. However, there is a group of companies who are formed solely with the intention of assisting you through the self-build process and, effectively, holding your hand along the way.

Package companies – also known as turnkey suppliers – will offer a specific service that is usually along the lines of providing both a design and project management services. They will in most cases also provide the structural frame (the vast majority of package suppliers provide timber frame kits) and will usually organise its construction. Some will also provide in-house labour to build the rest of the house, although most will offer a list of contractors.

To an extent it's possible to pick a house design you like out of a book and choose from a select list of materials (windows, flooring, internal doors, etc). However, most package companies offer bespoke design services (in the same way that an architect will) and many tend to end their interest in the project at weathertight stage or even before. Likewise, some of the European-based package suppliers offer a complete turnkey service, in part because they like to have control over the fitting of things like windows to achieve claimed higher build standards.

The package route is not for everyone – it's more expensive than the traditional architect/builder route, and most package suppliers tend to be strongly associated with a particular 'look' – but it can have its benefits. For a start, if you want a timber frame (more on which in Section Two) then chances are you will have to use a package supplier in some part. They tend to offer an invaluable advisory service – someone on your side – during the process itself, and are set up especially to deal with self-build beginners. If you want an oak frame, for example, you'd be well advised to engage with one of the handful of package suppliers. Another benefit is that package suppliers tend to minimise their upfront design costs, meaning that you won't have to find £1,000s from the word go.

CASE STUDY

TIMBER FRAME IMPORTED FROM GERMANY

PACKAGE HOUSE

### Cornish eco-build in three months

**ANDY AND ALISON Nicholls used Germany-based timber frame package supplier Baufritz for their Cornwall eco-friendly self-build project. The couple jetted out to the company's HQ to decide on everything about their home well in advance – from the external look to the choice of internal doors. After manufacture, the home's elements were driven into the UK along with a team of German workers who put the home together in less than three months. Andy and Alison were responsible for the foundations and final finishing off. "We wanted the Mercedes of houses and I think we got it. Nothing was left to chance, the build time was extraordinarily fast and the finishes are superb," says Andy.**

The build took just three months as the sections were delivered from Germany and craned into place. The Nicholls chose all the fittings and fixtures at the factory

Hard to believe that traditional this Cornish-stle home was created in a German factory

CASE STUDY

OAK FRAME PACKAGE

COUPLE CHANGED PLAN AS

# Garden plot was to good to miss

**JOHN HEAD AND KARIN** Skanberg were living in a modest 1960s bungalow in in West Sussex and planned to extend the property, but when the next-door neighbours decided to sell off their garden as a virgin building plot, the couple dropped everything and snapped up the land, which enjoys spectacular views to the South Downs. They used oak frame package supplier Border Oak to make and construct the oak frame and SIPS (Structural Insulated Panel) construction and used a main contractor for the rest of the project, with John and Karin pitching in with some DIY. This mixed approach is very popular with self-builders

You can get a mortgage to fund your self-build project in the same way as you would a normal house purchase

# WHAT IS SELF-BUILD?

## PART TWO

Caption for this house that was built for caption for house that Caption for this house that was built for caption for house that

# PART THREE

# COSTS & *finance*

## You don't have to be rich to build your own home

## *How it works*

In the same way that homeowners can spend anything from £50,000 to £5 million on their 'bought' home, so self-builders can spend the same creating their own home. The principle here is that you don't have to be rich to build your own home – people from all backgrounds and with all different income levels do it – but, as with anything in life, if you want the best and the biggest, you'll end up spending more. So while it's not realistic for those on a tight budget to expect to build a modern mansion, it is absolutely realistic for anyone who can get a mortgage to consider building a modest family home with a few individual touches that's better designed, and better quality, than they otherwise might be able to buy.

There are two significant costs when it comes to building your own home – the building plot and the house itself. When you buy a regular house, you are of course (in most cases) buying the land as well as the house, all factored into the same single price. So regional variances in house prices are not a factor of changing quality of the houses themselves so much as the value of the land it sits

# Building Plot Prices

Overall, the price of any building plot is decided by the value of a house built upon it. The more expensive the finished house, the more expensive the building plot. The price of a building plot (we're talking here about a piece of land with planning permission to build a house on it) can be influenced by several factors. Firstly, and most importantly, it depends on the location. In high-value property markets such as parts of the South-East, Cotswolds, Cheshire, for example, plot prices are likely to be higher than an equivalent site in, say, the North East, Lincolnshire or the Highlands. The differences can be huge – a plot that is an exact replica in terms of size, shape and quality which in Surrey might fetch £750,000 may well sell in Lincolnshire for £150,000. There are perfectly good plots available in the Highlands for less than £99,000. It's just that a house built on that Highland plot might be worth £180,000 compared to the finished house in Surrey being valued at £1.5m.

Size also affects a plot's value, although not by as much as you might think. The key factor really in establishing a general value is how big the house is that the plot has planning permission for. Again, it's a factor of the way size affects the end value of the house. So it's true to say that a large site with permission for a five bedroom house with large garden and annexes will fetch more than a small plot that has permission for, say a three bedroom house with a small front garden. Don't forget, though, that in many cases it is possible to get more bedrooms out of an existing planning permission. In the same way that a large house with a large garden on

*Size also affects a plot's value, abut not as much as you might think. The key factor in establishing a value is how big the house is that the plot has planning permission for.*

CASE STUDY

HOUSE ON A DISUSED URBAN FACTORY PLOT

## A CREATIVE APPROACH

This contemporary home in South East London exemplifies how self-builders can utilise the most unlikely bits of land. It has been built in place of a pair of garages – and it sailed through planning permission, largely on the basis that residents were happier to see a modern house rather than a pair of semi-derelict buildings. As a result of his ingenuity, the owner managed to get the land for well below the market rate and realised a massive uplift in his investment.

In order to maximise the relatively narrow plot, the house has been built in Structural Insulated Panels, which reduce the amount of space taken up by the walls

Building plot prices vary depending on the local housing market

the same street might fetch £200,000 more than a small house down the road, a large plot will be worth perhaps £50-100,000 more.

Sizes are often an abstract concept to people new to the idea of building your own home. To give some reference, most houses on modern housing developments are built on plots of between 1/12th and 1/20th of an acre. Typical self-build plots are in the region of 1/4 and 1/3 of an acre, allowing a modest front garden with drive and a decent back garden. A typical football pitch is around two acres in size, although bear in mind that acreage is a measurement of area not shape – meaning it's not necessarily rectangular.

Presentation will be a big factor in affecting a plot's value. An overgrown building plot that looks scrappy and problematic will cost less than one of the same size and shape in the same location that is flat and mowed. One of the best ways to get a bargain plot, indeed, is to look for unfashionable-looking plots in good areas.

While other factors may well influence a plot's price – such as proximity to services, or whether it has been previously developed, or is subject to a blight such as contamination – in essence, a plot's price is simply a function of the end value of the house that will sit on it. And just as it's impossible to say what it costs to buy a house, the same applies for plots.

To give some guidance, in a middle to high-value town or village expect to pay between £120-200,000 for a building plot. £300,000 will get you a large plot in most areas except high-value areas of the South East and Cheshire, where you could be spending £750,000.

CHEAP LAND

## PLANNING PERMISSION

**Don't consider buying cheap land that doesn't have planning permission if you realistically want to build your own home on it. Vendors are wise enough to sell their land with planning permission if it has a realistic chance of getting it, and so beware any 'plot' that seems too good to be true. You could always make purchase of the land subject to gaining satisfactory planning permission.**

# The Cost of Construction

Again, it varies wildly, but there are significant factors (location isn't really one of them).

**YOUR INVOLVEMENT.** The more you get involved, the lower the cost will be. So if you're going to be building your own home through DIY and designing it yourself too, then the cost is likely to be half that of a regular self-build. At the other end, using a turnkey supplier with minimal personal involvement is likely to be 10-30% more expensive than a regular architect/builder project.

*Using a turnkey supplier with minimal personal involvement is likely to be 10–30% more expensive than a regular architect/builder project.*

**SPECIFICATION.** This means the actual design and elements you decide to put into the house. You'll understand that it's difficult to give a general price for a house when houses vary so much – a kitchen alone can cost anything between £2,000 and £50,000. Likewise, the more complex the design details, the more difficult they are to achieve, the longer they take to get right, and therefore the more they cost to produce.

**SIZE.** Many construction costs are based on size. Buy flooring, for example, and you'll get quoted in cost/m². It's the same for many building jobs – the reason is to standardise the variance of size. It makes obvious sense that a small house costs less to build than a bigger house. So builders tend to work in costs/m².

With these factors taken into account, it's possible to build a good size four bedroom family home for around the £100-150,000 mark. DIY self-builders could do it, feasibly, for £50-100,000, depending on the specification. The average build cost of a self-build project in recent years has been in the low £200,000s.

## HOW TO GET STARTED

So what can you afford to build, how much should you spend on the plot, and how much is this thing going to cost you in total? Well, firstly, as you would with a regular home purchase, you need to work out what your budget is. This would typically be any equity or savings you have combined with the value of a mortgage you can get – ensuring you are comfortable with the payments, of course.

You'll then need to split your total budget into three elements – firstly, the cost of the plot; secondly, the cost of the house construction and lastly, an allowance for any unexpected expenditure, known as a contingency. But how much to allot to each? It's probably best to work back from an approximate (and generous) figure of how much you think it will cost to build your own home. We'll look much more in detail at build costs in Section Two, but as a general rule you should be expecting to pay £900-1,300/m² for your new home. A small four bedroom house might have a floor area of 150m² (still much bigger than the standard developer home) while a larger house might be 250m² up to 500m². Work out in general terms what you want (perhaps even speaking to a builder or package supplier at this stage to get a general idea on build costs) and what you expect to pay. Subtract this from your budget, along with another 10% for a contingency, and you're left with what you can afford to spend on a building plot.

**A TYPICAL BUDGET**

| | |
|---|---|
| **Value of Possible Mortgage:** | **£200,000** |
| **Savings/Equity:** | **£40,000** |
| **Total Budget:** | **£240,000** |
| **Estimated cost of building three bedroom home:** | **£140,000** |
| **10% Build Cost Contingency** | **£14,000** |
| **Remainder to Spend on a Plot:** | **£86,000** |

## WHAT TO DO IF YOUR BUDGET DOESN'T MATCH YOUR DREAMS

In the above example, our self-builders are left with just £86,000 to spend on a plot in their area. At this stage, the name of the game is compromise. If they are desperate to self-build and can't find plots in their area anywhere near their budget, they might want to move to a cheaper area; they might also determine to find a plot within their budget by knocking on doors and making offers on peoples' gardens. They might also decide that they need to increase their savings or equity by adding more value to their existing house to make a self-build project more realistic.

*Once you've built for the first time and that £240,000 spend has realised a home that is probably worth £300-350,000, then you'll have more to spend on the next.*

The key is to realise that a first self-built home is unlikely to be a dream, forever home. It's likely to be smaller than you might have dreamt of, without that home cinema or £50,000 kitchen; it might not have countryside views. However, once you've built for the first time and that £240,000 spend has realised a home that is probably worth £300-350,000, then you'll have more to spend on the next. It usually takes three self-builds to end up in the home of your dreams.

CASE STUDY

TIMBER FRAME HOUSE BUILT FOR £134,000

## SIMPLE BUT EFFECTIVE DESIGN

On a remarkably low budget, Terry Morgan has shown what can be achieved if you have good local contacts, shop around for the best prices and use a simple but effective design. He has built a $174m^2$, four bed house in a Conservation Area in one of the most expensive parts of the country for just £134,000. What is more, he has added a number of traditional characterful features – normally reserved for builds with bigger budgets.

Built in an Oxfordshire village for a low price

# *How will you fund your build project?*

You will need access to money to pay for the building plot and stamp duty, pay all the upfront design fees, and fund the project as it goes along – paying for labour and materials. How you find this money will, of course, depend on your unique situation.

## EQUITY RELEASE

If you want to stay in your existing house while you at least start the self-build process, then you could investigate the possibility of using some of the equity you might

First time self-builder Caron Pain managed her own self-build project and spent just £110,000

have in your current home – effectively taking the profit early. Lenders will usually let you borrow in the region of up to 66-75% of the equity you have built up in your home (equity being the difference between your mortgage and the current value), often at the same or similar lending rate to the rest of your mortgage. So if your property is worth £300,000 and your mortgage is £200,000, your equity is £100,000 you could borrow in the region of £70,000. In essence, it is a cheap and relatively low-risk way to fund the early stages of a project while at the same time minimising upheaval, although there is always the possibility that in the period between releasing equity and you eventually selling the property the end value has fallen (although this is why lenders only offer a relatively low percentage of the equity for release). It's certainly true that a combination of equity and some savings might well cover the purchase of land, though.

*Many lenders quote a Loan to Value (LTV) based on the finished value. This percentage figure varies week-by-week and lender by lender, but in general it's around 85% of the three key values.*

## HIGH STREET LENDERS & BUILDING SOCIETIES

For those looking for funding for a self-build project, it is usually worth a conversation with your regular bank manager. After all, they are likely to know your financial situation best of all and you may well have established a trusted relationship with them (possibly too with your mortgage provider, if different). While surprisingly few of the big name banks provide formal facilities for self-build finance, many can usually come to a more informal arrangement to help you finance the project, perhaps through an overdraft facility that then gets turned into a mortgage, or through some other loan vehicle. The most common means however is through the bank's commercial lending arm – they will treat you as they would a commercial housing developer asking them for financial help – and there's every possibility this is a route that might appeal, although interest rates on commercial loans might be 1-3% higher than private mortgages.

## SELF-BUILD MORTGAGES

A mortgage for a self-build project is specially tailored towards the unique way you 'pay' for your finished house (in several instalments, rather than all at once on completion day) and as a result you might need a specialist, experienced self-build mortgage provider. Self-build mortgages are unique in that they release the agreed sum in various stages. Firstly, of course, you'll get money to cover the majority of the cost of the building plot; then you'll get a series of 'stage payments', usually released in advance of work starting, to cover payments to your builder or package supplier at agreed stages (such as floor structure, wall plate, weathertight and so on). You will only be charged interest on the money you've borrowed to date, and it's likely that you will then convert the self-build mortgage to a regular house mortgage upon completion of the project, subject to valuation.

You will be able to borrow money based on the provider's regular criteria (e.g. four times single income or two times joint) up to certain percentage of the value of the land, and a certain percentage of the value of the expected build costs, in total not making up more than a certain percentage of the finished value of the house. Many lenders simply quote a maximum Loan to Value (LTV) based on the finished value. This percentage figure varies enormously week-by-week and lender by lender, but in general terms it's around 85% of the three key values. So you'll need to find 15% of the cost of the land and 15% of the cost of the build, which combined should be no more than 15% of the end value of the house (as the combined cost of the plot and build is usually much less than the end value of the house, this isn't really a problem).

**EXAMPLE**

**PLOT cost £180,000: (85% LTV) so lender covers £153,000, self-builder funds £27,000**

**BUILD cost £150,000 (85% LTV) so lender covers £127,500, self-builder funds £22,500.**

What's interesting in this example – based on a modest to average expectation of what a plot and project might cost – the self-builder will need to bring in the region of £50,000 to the table, with a total mortgage of £280,500. At an interest rate of 5% on a 25 year interest only mortgage

# *I'm worried about costs spiralling out of control!*

It's all too easy to assume that the vast majority of self-builders end up going massively over their initial budgets – which, for those on modest incomes, could be potentially disastrous. Excessive costs usually occur due to bad project planning – more of which in the next section – but it certainly isn't the case that all self-build projects are set on a course for budget overload.

*Many projects end up going over budget because the budget in the first instance was completely unrealistic for the design and specification of the project*

## DESIGN

Many projects end up going over budget because the budget in the first instance was completely unrealistic for the design and specification of the project. Meaning, that the design was too big, or too complex, and that the designer involved had insufficient knowledge of the end costs. A designer should, of course, be well-trained in recognising how to design a house set for your own budget and it should be viewed by the potential self-builder as just as important a part of the process as the exterior look. Always ensure your budget is at the heart of any design decision.

**The key to making sure you keep costs down is to ensure the house is designed with your budget in mind, both in terms of size and complexity**

## BE DETAILED AND ACCURATE IN YOUR PLANS

Perhaps the number one reason why projects end up going over budget is that not enough detail was provided at the 'tender' stage (when builders provide a quote based on a set of drawings and list of materials to go into the project). The more 'unknowns' you provide (say, you might not have yet decided on bathroom arrangements) then the more likely the builder is to need extra payment to cover the extra work – not to mention additional materials that you will require. An easy way of explaining this is that, if you haven't yet decided on your kitchen, the builder might allow a 'PC sum' (it means Prime Cost sum, and is a pencil-in figure) of £8,000, but if the kitchen of your dreams costs £20,000, you're already £12,000 over budget.

## THE IMPORTANCE OF THE CONTINGENCY

It's obviously less dramatic to go over budget if you've prepared for it. It's always good to allow 10-15% of your build budget as a contingency to set against additional expenditure that, unlike expensive kitchens, you can't foresee. This is particularly used up in additional foundation costs, and is a useful hedge against your budget going slightly over.

CASE STUDY

BUDGET BUNGALOW

## THIS ONLY COST £80K

**Will Hearsey and Lynsey Woods built their bungalow for just £80,000 – thanks in part down to careful planning. "We had spent an evening working out exactly what it should cost to build, right down to the exact number of bricks," explains Will. "We didn't really shop around for materials, but bought almost everything from Jewson, including the bathrooms and kitchen. It meant that they could afford to give us a generous discount and deliveries were simplified.**

The cost of the kitchen, bathroom, flooring and finishes is kep to keeping to a budget

# PART FOUR

# Building PLOTS

## The First Piece In The Jigsaw

## What is a Building Plot?

The starting point in the whole process is, of course, the land on which to build your new home. The individual nature of the land itself will dictate the size and shape of your house and quite possibly its end value – it really is the starting point for the whole process. And there are some things that you need to know in order to understand the world of building plots – most of all planning permission.

For a start, it's worth making clear that you need a building plot – not just any old bit of land. You can't simply build a house on any random bit of land you might have bought off a farmer, for instance – a bit of land is not a building plot unless it has full planning permission to build a house on it.

The building plot you will end up buying is likely to fall into one of three categories.

### GARDEN

Owners of houses with large (especially side) gardens

might want to cash in on its value by applying for planning permission for a house to be built on it. The reason for this is that land without planning permission is usually at least 10 times less valuable than land with approval.

## REPLACEMENT DWELLINGS

When you consider that houses all around you are merely temporary occupants of building plots, then you begin to see the potential in replacement dwellings. This is particularly viable when the existing house might be underdeveloped according to the size of the plot, or it might be in a poor state of repair. And, contrary to popular belief, it's not terribly expensive to demolish an existing house – usually between £5-10,000, not taking into account the potential value of any bricks, tiles etc salvageable from the site itself.

## VIRGIN LAND

Occasionally councils release new bits of land – perhaps previously scrubland or farmland – for development. These are known as virgin or 'greenfield' plots and in most cases would be sold as regular building plots.

Unless they already own the plot of land – it's worth noting that many self-builders actually go on to build on land they already own (how big is your garden?) or even knock down their existing house – then in reality finding a building plot can be a difficult and drawn-out process. There is a definite shortage in supply of suitable one-off plots and for many self-builders this is likely to be the most frustrating part of the process – and a hurdle that many never successfully negotiate.

WARNING

### WHEN IS A PLOT NOT A PLOT?

**A building plot is not a building plot unless it has up-to-date planning permission with it. Some plots might have enjoyed permission to build in the past but, as planning approval only lasts five years, might now be lapsed. Local planning policies change all the time, and so there's no guarantee that what once got planning approval will do so again.**

CASE STUDY

SMALL SIDE GARDEN

# Small plots can have potential

**Warren and Jocelyn Milne spent a long time looking for the right building plot for them. For a year and a half, they knocked on the doors of those with large gardens, scoured websites and pestered estate agents. "We looked at a lot of places," says Warren. Finally they alighted upon a small plot in the town of Slough. Not the most prepossessing of sites but, at £190,000 including an existing three bedroom house, just about within their means. "It was more of a practical choice than a heart choice," says Warren "We had a limited budget and this meant we got a house plus the land down the side of it, which had permission for a two bedroom house."**

Long search paid off for the Milnes

The three storey home really maximises the possibilities of the tiny side garden building plot

# *The Planning System*

In order to successfully look for a building plot you have to have a basic understanding of the planning system. Before the introduction of the Town and Country Planning Act in 1947, there was no formal system of controlling development in the United Kingdom – meaning effectively that anyone could build a house wherever they pleased. Previous to the 1947 Act, ownership a piece of land in itself conferred the right to develop it. The Act introduced the requirement for planning permission, and so the modern system was introduced as a means of implementing central and local controls on development – to this day, the planning system is set up in order to stop and control development rather than encourage it.

*To this day, the planning system is set up in order to stop and control development r ather than encourage it.*

In essence, the system we have today is best described as a series of boundaries – they might be called Local Development Plans or something similar in your area – that show where development is allowed in relation to an existing city, town, village or hamlet. Inside that boundary, there is a presumption towards allowing development, subject to conditions of the design of the development itself. Outside it – in what might be termed the 'countryside' or even 'Green Belt' – the chances of gaining permission to build a new house are practically zero.

What the planning system also does, of course, is create huge variances in the value of land that might in all other ways share the same factors. A one acre site might be worth twenty times the one acre site next door to it if that first bit of land enjoys planning approval.

Once you have bought a plot, the planning system will become much more relevant in deciding the exact details of the house you'll end up building.

**WHEN PLOTS MEET PLANNERS**

## WAYS IN WHICH PLANNING SHOULD AFFECT YOUR SEARCH

**1. You see a 'building plot' advertised for sale. If it's a plot, it should have current planning approval. Ask to see the approved plans and check to see they are in date and broadly match your aspirations.**

**2. You identify a piece of land that might be suitable. Use the planning system to identify whether or not it is within the existing development boundary (either by calling the local authority planning office directly or checking on their website) and, as a result, whether it has a realistic chance of gaining approval. Make any future offer subject to gaining approval.**

### FACT

**Because gaining planning approval on a previously undeveloped site or a garden might be seen as controversial – neighbours for one are likely to object – landowners who apply for planning permission prior to selling a 'building plot' are more likely to apply for permission to build a small, simple house, or even a bungalow. The less controversial or large the design, the less likely it is to be rejected. However, the potential plot purchaser can then apply for permission to build the house they want without jeopardising the initial permission. In theory, you can apply for planning permission as many times as you want.**

**Building by a river presents challenges but also opportunities for interesting design. This self-build by the River Thames incorporates a boat mooring**

Although the planners insisted that this new self-built home be a bungalow, the owners got three storeys out of it by building a basement level and using the large roof space for bedrooms

# *A Beginner's Reference Guide*

## SIZES

Building plots haven't gone metric and are usually quoted in acres. One acre is 4,046m², or 4,840 square yards – the equivalent of a piece of land measuring, for example, around 35 metres wide by 115 metres deep. To get a mental picture of its size, an acre is about the equivalent of two standard size football pitches.

Most plots are much smaller than this and common sizes are 1/4, 1/3 or 1/2 of an acre – plenty of space for a large home and good garden. Bear in mind that average 'estate' developer plots are often between 1/10 and 1/15 of an acre.

## SERVICES

Your house needs to have power in order to work and all but the most rural sites will aim to connect to some or all of the mains services – water, sewerage and electricity and, depending on how far it is away from the grid, gas. In general, it's a positive to have services already on site or within touching distance – connecting to distant service runs will be an additional and unpredictable cost.

## PLANNING TYPES

You might see a plot advertised with 'OPP' or 'DPP' or even 'Full' planning permission. These are abbreviations of the different types of planning status that a site might have.

OPP stands for Outline Planning Permission. A landowner may apply for approval in principle to build a house on a plot of land. Agreement is granted in outline. In order to build a house, you would need to get the details of an actual design scheme agreed – which is

CASE STUDY

TWO BEDROOM HOUSE COSTING £84K, LAND £25K

Built in place of an old run-down cottage, Ann's new home cost just £84,000 to construct

# Brilliance on a very tight budget

**ANN DONOVAN SELF-BUILT HER TWO** bedroom 94 sq m cottage in South Wales on a tiny budget. Despite the site being small and awkwardly-shaped, there was already an old cottage in place and Ann persuaded the planners to let her knock it down and build a traditional style home in its place. Funded from savings earmarked for a future pension (which was then topped back up when she sold her previous house) Ann used a local builder to complete the construction. "It's designed exactly for my needs," she says.

# The first piece in the jigsaw

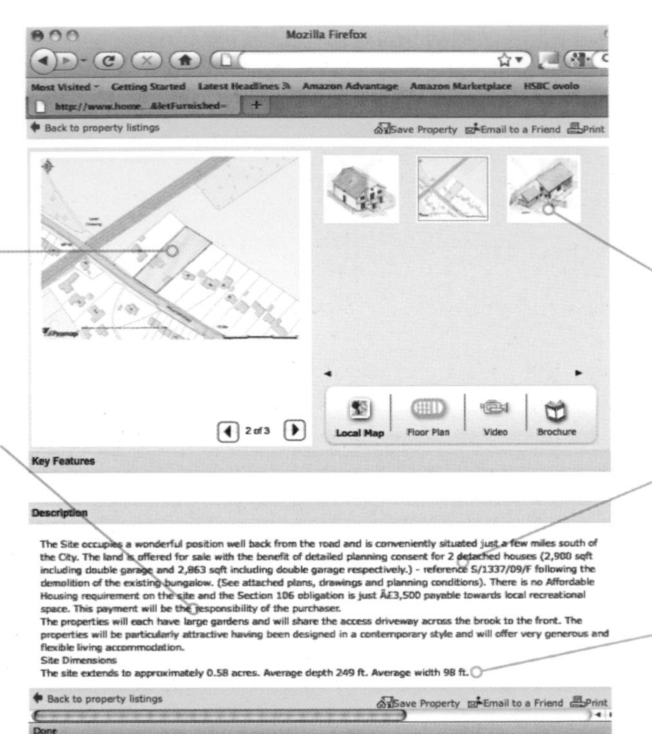


Details on almost all available building plots can be viewed online. Try plotfinder.net to search in your area

The outlined area is the piece of land that is for sale

The description will mention any issues particular to the site, for example any local payments that need to be made

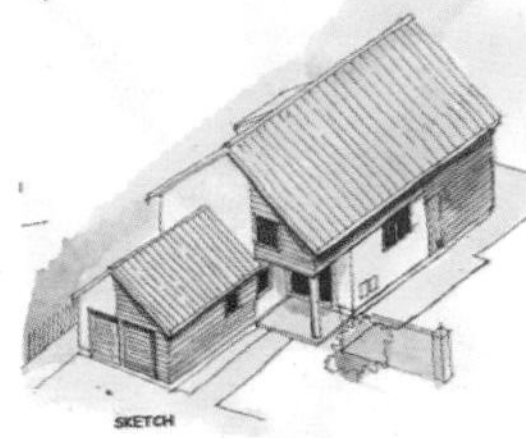


Look for any drawings of the permitted plans. You can always reapply for something you want but this is a good indication as to the type of house the planners want to see

Use the particulars to double check that the plot still has a valid planning permission. You should find a reference on the description

The description will also give an approximate size (always worth checking before purchase). 0.58 of an acre allows room for a large garden

Detailed Planning Permission, or DPP.

Some landowners might bypass the process of outline/ detailed by simply applying for the complete scheme from the start (indeed some local authorities now insist on this for controversial sites). This is known as Full Planning Permission.

**BEWARE**

## INVESTMENT LAND

**There are several companies that sell so-called 'investment' land, targeting investors or self-builders (also known as landbanking schemes). They usually specialise in slicing up a large field on the edge of an existing development into small plots which are then sold off at too-good-to-be-true prices on the basis that they will rocket in value once planning permission has been granted. Unfortunately the chances of planning permission ever being granted on these plots is beyond minimal and so they are best avoided by anyone serious about finding a plot.**

Not all building plots are presented very well. Imagine the house that's going to be there, rather than judging the purchase on the existing state

# Plot costs and how to judge value

How much should you pay for a plot? Well, it all depends on just one thing: the end value of the house that ends up being built upon it. The higher the end value, the higher the value of the plot it sits on. You can work out the value of a building plot by getting the completed house valued by an estate agent (they can usually come up with an approximate figure off any plans or description), subtracting the expected build costs (see section two) and taking away another 10-20% (which should be the profit enjoyed by the developer of the land). The resulting figure is the true value of the plot.

Plots obviously vary in price across the country depending on the local property market, with the most expensive plots in the country being in the Home Counties and parts of the South East, parts of Hampshire and Dorset, and the so-called 'Footballer's Belt' around Cheshire. In general, where house prices are high, plot prices follow. The cheapest parts of the country to buy a plot are the Scottish Highlands and remote parts of Lincolnshire, in addition to the less attractive areas of all major cities.

*The most expensive plots are in the Home Counties, parts of the South East, parts of Hampshire and Dorset, and the so-called 'Footballer's Belt' around Cheshire*

## WHERE TO FIND A PLOT

We'll look more in depth at the art of finding a suitable plot in Section Two of this book, but there are some starting points.

Firstly, use the common routes that you would take when looking for a house – the internet search engines, property pages in your local newspaper, registering with agents for updates. Bear in mind, however, that only a few of the main agents in any town will deal with building plots and in many cases you'll need to find the local land surveyors or auction houses to get the complete picture. Also, bear in mind that simply registering your details with an agent and expecting a call to let you know of the range of plots they have on offer simply isn't realistic – finding a plot is a competitive world.

Many building plots end up being sold through auction houses – it's a fast and effective way for vendors to realise a plot's value. Again, register with all of the main auction houses (including the national property auction houses who specialise in repossessions, former

PLOTS ON THE MARKET

### EXAMPLES OF RECENTLY-SOLD PLOTS

PART FIVE

# HOUSE *design basics*

## An Individual Home, Created Just for You

One of the main reasons why people are attracted to the idea of building their own home is because they struggle to find a home on the regular market that suits their own needs.

Building your own home is the only way to end up with a home that is created bespoke, just for you and your family. Something that's off-the-shelf might be good but there will always be some form of compromise – whether it's a simple thing like the size of the bedrooms or the garden.

Getting something on the market that's a perfect fit is very difficult – which is why so few homes available are ever worth considering. You might have three children – meaning you need at least four bedrooms. Ideally, to avoid the morning rush for the shower, you would need three bathrooms – with one for yourself. You might work from home occasionally and therefore need a home office; you might also have elderly parents who you're considering have move in with you, ideally to an annexe. You feel that you want a large kitchen where the family

One of the main reasons people build their own homes is to create living spaces that you wouldn't be able to find in a home built by a developer

This luxury contemporary-style home in Surrey is at the very top end of self-builders' dreams, complete with swimming pool and plenty of glazing

can eat, but aren't bothered by a dining room; you would love a 'snug' living room surrounded by books.

It sounds pretty specific, doesn't it? Well, many would argue that your home really is the most important thing you own. It seems that in every aspect of our lives we have become discerning consumers; we research car purchases for months, assessing the wide range of choices and end up with something that fits perfectly. It's the same with everything else, from clothes to gadgets.

Yet when it comes to buying a house – the biggest purchase any of us will ever make – we seem perfectly happy to compromise. We'll compromise on the size of the rooms, or the size of the garden, or the number of bathrooms, or the lack of a home office, or any of the other things mentioned above. We might eventually extend or remodel to try and address these issues, but that's rather missing the point.

It might not just be something as simple as the size or number of rooms that you end up discarding. More and more we like our homes to look good, to be architecturally interesting and correct, and to be finished well. It only takes a cursory look around any modern housing estate to realise that mainstream housing developers are creating houses that simply don't stand up to architectural scrutiny. Most of them are built these days in a kind of mock Georgian style – marketing research has shown that Georgian is the most popular choice with potential buyers. But developers don't really prioritise architectural design – and it shows. The windows are usually in the wrong position and too small or large, and they're usually the wrong windows anyway; the roof pitch is usually out and the bricks are often some of the

**Designed around a modern woodburner, this living room has been designed to let in plenty of light**

cheapest and least characterful available. Inside, ceiling heights are considerably squatter than an authentic Georgian style would require and, in most cases, the layouts and room sizes seem to give up on the whole Georgian pretence altogether.

For this reason, most people who have an eye for house design tend therefore to favour older houses – many Georgian, Edwardian and Victorian originals look absolutely perfect, with all of the detailing mentioned above absolutely 'right' – inside and out. The problem is that many of them don't provide the performance and basic requirements homeowners demand of their homes these days. They are probably short of a bathroom or two, particularly upstairs; the realities of maintenance can become frightening and, perhaps most significantly of all, they are difficult and expensive to keep warm. Once invasive surgery is undertaken to address these issues, whether it be in the form of an extension to create extra space or adding insulation to improve the home's performance, it's difficult to avoid taking something away from the appeal of the period home itself – extensions rarely look any good.

*Developers are creating houses that simply don't stand up to architectural scrutiny. Most of them are built in a kind of mock Georgian style*

But to argue, as many people do, that new homes as a rule can't look great is simply not true. People create architecturally outstanding individual new homes all the time up and down the country and

# An individual home, created for you

A modern street-frontage that is all about security – the rear enjoys great views over countryside

all around the world – in a huge range of styles. There are many talented architects who can create amazing cutting-edge designs that have their roots in the modernist style – all big windows and flat roofs – or the organic architectural school pioneered by Frank Lloyd Wright, incorporating more natural materials but in a strong modern style. Many architectural critics argue that it is really only authentic to build new homes that are truly 21st century in style, and it's these homes that look best of all. If it wasn't for modern architecture, of course, then features that we now pretty much universally aspire to such as open plan living and a blurred boundary between inside and outside spaces wouldn't have taken off.

However, if you do love period design, whatever the period, then you can achieve a new home that is absolutely indistinguishable in look from an authentic original and has the added benefit of incorporating the number of bathrooms you need, as well as those all-important energy-efficiency measures such as plenty of insulation and double glazing. Indeed, the majority of people who create individual homes opt for a period design and usually the first thing they say is that passers-by comment on what a lovely renovation project it is!

The fact is that building a home from scratch is the only way to get the best of all worlds – a home that is of the highest architectural merit, one that has the exact space and room requirements you want, and has all the benefits of the very best modern construction techniques. Many people come to self-build out of necessity – they might have specific special needs that only a bespoke home can give them, for instance – but the majority come to the conclusion that, when you believe the home is the most important place, then it really should be made just for you.

Many self-builders want to live in modern homes built in traditional styles, such as this fine Georgian style home

Planners are increasingly encouraging self-builders to embrace modern designs that incorporate outdoor spaces into the living accommodation

# *The design process explained*

Although many people quite understandably spend hours dreaming of the home they are going to create for themselves, any house design by definition has to be a specific reaction to an individual site and location. As a result, it's best to spend the time before you find a plot thinking in general terms about the styles of house you like and what you might include – but leave the specifics until you find the plot itself.

The reason for this is that building plots are rarely uniform in size or shape. They might be flat or sloping. There might be different architectural precedents on different local streets. Above all, they face in different directions and your plot's orientation will (or should) have an impact on the position of rooms. That's not to mention that you might want to take account of a view from the plot or avoid overlooking a neighbour. All of these things will help a designer formulate the final design of your new home.

WHAT TO DO

## THE PROCESS

- **Buy a plot**
- **Find and interview designers**
- **Come up with a design scheme that you're happy with and confident can be built to your budget**
- **Submit the design to the planning department for approval**
- **Upon approval, you'll need a full set of technical building drawings, based on your specific plans, to send out to builders and submit for conditional building regulations approval**
- **Start work**

## HOW TO GET A HOUSE DESIGN

For most self builders, the design process is the most exciting part of the whole experience. After years of 'making do' you're finally drawing up plans for your new, perfect, family home. As with the construction of the house itself, however, there are several different ways to approach this part of the project.

## ARCHITECT

First things first – the term 'architect' is protected by law and while all architects are designers, not all designers are qualified Architects. Only designers who have been through the seven years of training, passed their exams and registered with the Architects Registration Board can call themselves Architects – and they are very protective about the title.

Architects are not universally experienced in all aspects of design. Some might specialise in commercial design and some in residential. As a result, you'll need to find an architect who is experienced in house design and preferably in the style of design you are interested in. You'll want to interview two or three candidates in the same way you would with builders.

Having decided to go ahead with an architect, you have the choice of how to proceed – either simply paying a fixed fee for design work, or a percentage of total build cost (usually between 8-12%) for design work and on-site supervision of the contract. This would involve the architect helping you to recruit a builder and ensuring the work on site matches the design vision.

The key to success in this route is in clarifying your expectations of, and relationship with, the architect from the start. Many people have bad experiences with architects who simply present them with a fait accompli scheme that doesn't meet their expectations. Bear in mind that the key to avoiding this is a detailed brief and clarifying your expectations of what the architect is going to produce. If you're not happy with what you receive back (and bear in mind that the design process is usually a process of gradual evolution rather than instant success) then keep on working together. It also pays to be clear about when payment is expected – how much, and when.

**FIND AN ARCHITECT**

You can search for suitable architects at www.architecture.com or alternatively contact Associated Self-build Architects (as the name suggests, qualified architects who specialise in dealing with self-build clients) at www.asba-architects.org

**FIND AN ARCHITECTURAL TECHNOLOGIST**

You can find Architect Technologists at The Chartered Institute of Architectural Technologists (www.ciat.org.uk). Individual house designers tend to advertise in the self-build magazines, the Yellow Pages and local newspapers.

**PACKAGE COMPANIES**

There is no national association of package companies. They advertise in self-build magazines, exhibit at Homebuilding & Renovating shows and online.

## ARCHITECTURAL TECHNOLOGISTS AND HOUSE DESIGNERS

Technologists and designers (i.e. designers not qualified as architects) offer many of the design skills and experience that architects provide and often in a format more in keeping with the expectations of a novice private client wanting a house design.

The process is the same as above although it's more likely to be a fixed fee for design work than a supervisory role in which you'll engage them.

Don't be put off because designers haven't been through the seven years training and finished all their exams. A title is much less important than an ability to listen to your requirements and employ a wealth of experience – indeed many of the very best one-off houses are designed by people without qualifications.

## PACKAGE COMPANIES

Self-build package companies, as you might guess, offer an in-house design service as part of the deal. All of

They may not be to everyone's taste, but contemporary style homes benefit from lots of light and innovative, eye-catching design

them offer brochures to give you an idea of the houses they build and some companies specialise in certain styles. Indeed, if you want a brand new oak framed home built in a Tudor style, you're best to use one of the oak frame package companies. Although some package companies offer standard designs out of a brochure, the vast majority now offer a bespoke design service utilising either in-house or even freelance designers. Many of these designers are the most experienced creators of individual houses you can find – and a valuable resource.

The package company design process remains the same as it would if you're using a regular house designer. However, the payment element is more convenient. Most package companies tend to include the design cost within the overall contract cost so whilst it's not free, it does minimise the upfront costs of house design.

It's worth noting too that you can't engage with a package company for their design work and then use the design elsewhere. Package companies view their design service as an attractive sweetener and as a result retain strict controls over use of their plans.

## DESIGN IT YOURSELF

There is nothing stopping you from designing your own home. You don't have to be qualified or even registered to carry out design work – unlike some other aspects of construction – and it goes without saying that you could potentially save £1,000s in design fees.

But before you race off and try and find your old school set square – give it some serious thought. House designers bring experience and skills to the process that you won't have, and in addition to avoiding design mistakes that will be impossible or at the very least expensive to rectify later,

Light from above plays a key part in making self-built homes more pleasant to live in than regular homes

they will be able to give valuable advice on designing to a specific build cost. Something that you, dear amateur Frank Lloyd Wright, won't have.

Similarly, one of the key elements of the planning application process is the presentation of the plans itself. Despite computer software packages becoming more sophisticated in recent years, nothing quite compares with a well presented drawing of a new home.

House design is about a lot more than getting all the rooms in the right position and making it look 'like a house'. The key to a successful, attractive design is largely in the detail – window surrounds, positioning of rainwater goods, brick arches and canopies – and these are all things that the inexperienced DIYer may get wrong.

*Despite computer software packages becoming more sophisticated in recent years, nothing quite compares with a beautifully presented drawing of a new home.*

Lastly, a professional designer will also produce a set of working, technical drawings for the builder to follow. They will show the position of floor joists and the size of lintels required. Again, it's highly unlikely you'll have this knowledge and getting it wrong can be extremely costly.

So it's easy to see how those few thousand pounds that you feel you're saving by avoiding a professional designer can be quickly spent on silly mistakes. Design really is the fundamental element of a self-build project and if all of those months on site, not to mention large amounts of money, are not focussed on creating something truly special and perfect for you, then the whole affair really is a bit of a waste of time.

## HOW MUCH WILL A HOUSE DESIGN COST?

For a full service – including contract administration and the full 'hand-holding' game, an Architect will charge between 7-10% of the build cost, whereas for a partial service, which might just include the initial design work, they tend to work on an agreed hourly rate, which will depend on the size of the project. RIBA quote between £55-150/hour for design work, and clients would be expecting to pay £5-10,000 for work on this basis. Fees are not that different between Architects and Technologists but the world of house designers contains a huge disparity in fees.

You could easily find someone willing to charge less than £1,000 for plans drawing services; while the more experienced and accomplished designers might well charge as much as an Architect. Whether it's a fixed fee or an hourly rate will usually depend on how much work goes into the scheme (they'll usually put you on an hourly rate if there's lots of negotiation involved.) In general, whoever you go to, you should expect to pay between £5-10,000 for design fees. As mentioned, this may be as low as £1,000, or it may be as high as – one self-builder was quoted this from a leading London firm – £50,000. It's worth noting too that despite the common conception, Architects aren't getting rich out of their work (usually). According to the RIBA Salary Survey 2009, more than a fifth of architects are out of work, and average earnings are £45,000.

The designer of this home visited the site to work out the best orientation

# Formulating a design brief

The key to getting a design that meets your specific needs is to come up with a detailed brief – this is the guidance a designer will have as to what you want out of a house. It's difficult to overemphasise just how important this element of the whole self-build process is: things are easier to change on plan than on site, and impossible to alter once you've moved in. So approach the design stage very methodically.

Many designers (and particularly package companies) experienced in working with self-builders will guide you through this process. They may ask you to provide cut-outs from magazines of houses, spaces and specific design features that you like. They will also ask you describe your lifestyle as best as possible to them – meaning how and when you use your existing home, and also what you envisage most about your new life. In simpler terms, they will also ask you for a simple list of room requirements. However, it is worth trying to come up with a brief yourself – at the very least it will help you formulate your ideas.

*You may be asked to provide cut-outs from magazines of houses, spaces and design features that you like. They will also ask you how and when you use your existing home*

## UNDERSTAND YOUR VISION

Try and picture first of all what you want out of your new home. Aim to capture the visual dream it is you're really aiming for – whether it be a large kitchen that the family congregates in after work and school, or a master bedroom suite that incorporates a dressing room. It might be a simple thing like a dedicated home cinema, or a living room that opens out onto a patio in summer. Most people self-build because they can picture a lifestyle in their new home. Write it down and provide visual clues if necessary.

Rebecca and Jim Dyer, both architects, designed their own contemporary home in Somerset

# An individual home, created for you

Architects can incorporate features like integrated sunrooms

## YOUR FAMILY

You should list all the family members, with ages, who will be using the house. Do they have any specific needs or wants – and how many bedrooms and bathrooms would you like. Do any of them have desires for particular features – e.g. a home office for home working, a games room or even a home gym. List all the rooms the family wants and how they are to be used. If you have a young family, for instance, you might want a room where the kids can play and leave their toys around without it being in full view of everyone.

## DESIGN ISSUES

Although the designer will visit your site, it's worth noting any other specific issues that need considering in a design. For example, if there is a noisy road to the front, then the key bedrooms might want to be placed at the back. Make the designer aware of any good views, or the positioning of a protected tree. Also list what parking and garage requirements you have, and the need to incorporate any energy-efficiency measures.

## WHAT YOU LIKE IN A HOUSE

Here's where you let the designer know how you want the house to feel and what it should be like to live in. Do you want to incorporate architectural space like a double height area, or different floor levels? Do you like open plan layouts or more defined rooms? Would you like, in general, a more modern look or something a bit more traditional. What about fireplaces? It might be best to go through the self-build magazines (which tend to capture spaces more than the mainstream home interest magazines, which largely concentrate on furniture) to cut out pictures and details you like.

## EXTERNAL LOOK

Although the way your home looks from the outside will not be completely under your control – it is much more likely to be influenced by local planners, who might look to neighbouring properties for precedents – you should express some preference for the overall style you want your new home to be built in. Do you like a particular style – whether it be Contemporary/Modernist, Georgian, Tudor, Edwardian, Arts & Crafts, Art Deco, Cottage Style, or something else? If you do decide to choose a particular style, bear in mind that getting that style architecturally correct is going to be fundamental to how successful your project is. See following pages for a quick guide to the main styles.

## SPECIFICATION REQUIREMENTS

Now is the time to let your designer know about any particular specification details that you would like to include. Don't just concentrate on the key design features, such as a walk-in shower enclosure or a split staircase, but also things like windows. If they are of an unusual shape or size, they need to be incorporated in at the design stage. The earlier you can make the key decisions, the better.

# *The different house design styles*

## COTTAGE

The classic cottage is a quintessentially English design style and one that endures to this day. Cottages are rural by nature and built simply, preferably using local materials and techniques (early examples may be built using local cob or mud). As a result, some might have thatched roofs, but all will have small windows and are usually of single storey, perhaps with rooms built into the roof. They are clad in whatever material is available locally – possibly stone or a lime-based render. Internally the layout is likely to be simple and fairly open, with few rooms – perhaps an open kitchen and living space and a separate sitting area. Cottages are cosy in essence and should incorporate fireplaces and exposed structural details, such as beams

# An individual home, created for you

## TUDOR

Designed around the growing use of timber in house construction, tudor homes are characterised by exposed timber frames externally, usually on both storeys. They tend to incorporate some gable ends and a steeply pitched roof, with small windows and large chimneys. Inside they might take on a mediaeval feel, possibly incorporating a Great Hall – a central dining hall that is overlooked by a gallery – and almost certainly grand bedrooms open to the roof structure. Today's poorer imitations replace the structural timber frame with a decorative timber effect – the dreaded Mock Tudor synonymous with suburban stockbroker belts.

## GEORGIAN

The Georgian style remains the most enduring and popular of all the house design styles through the ages. Georgian homes are famed for their simplicity and symmetry and, in a way, it is this that makes them favoured by developers – for in the simplicity comes ease (and value) of construction. The symmetry has a certain formality about it which gives Georgian homes a certain sense of grandeur – the double frontage is particularly popular. Part of this is because Georgian design has its roots in Classicism – all columns and porticos, but it has various unique elements depending on the exact period as the style evolved over 120 years.

## VICTORIAN

As with most styles, Victorian primarily reacted against the predominant Georgian style before it. Victorian homes were often asymmetrical, with steeply pitched roofs and dominant gable ends. This was not so much the era of the country pile, more the mass produced urban home, built for workers in the booming manufacturing industries. Built on smaller plots, they tend to be more vertical than their predecessors. Internally, Victorian homes are known for their tall ceiling heights and use of corridors.

## ARTS & CRAFTS

Reacting against the engineered coldness of Victorian design, with its emphasis on standardization and machinery, the Arts & Crafts style, which was around at the turn of the 19th and 20th centuries, reintroduced the concept of artisan craftsmanship into house construction. It is rustic, natural and homely and inspired by rural England, as opposed to the classical roots of Georgian design. External features consist of strong, steep roofs and dominant gables; bays and heavy buttresses and chimneys. They might be clad in a mix of tile hanging and render, but almost all have clay roof tiles and leaded windows. This is a busy style – it's asymmetrical and roof lines are complex.

## MODERNIST

Homes built in the modernist style tend to have flat roofs and long, horizontal windows letting in plenty of light. They are usually simple and strong in terms of shape with a minimum of fussy detailing - often clad in a simple white render with guttering and downpipes hidden away, minimal window framing, and so on. Internally, they tend to be light and open, with no small corridors and an open plan layout.

## ORGANIC

This style is still highly contemporary – often daring in terms of roof shape, incorporating innovative engineering features such as large curves and long, low overhanging roofs – but has a softer feel that reflects it being a little closer to nature. Organic architecture will pay more attention to sustainable design principles than other styles. Houses of this style are often clad in timber and have large windows to maximise the amount of solar gain.

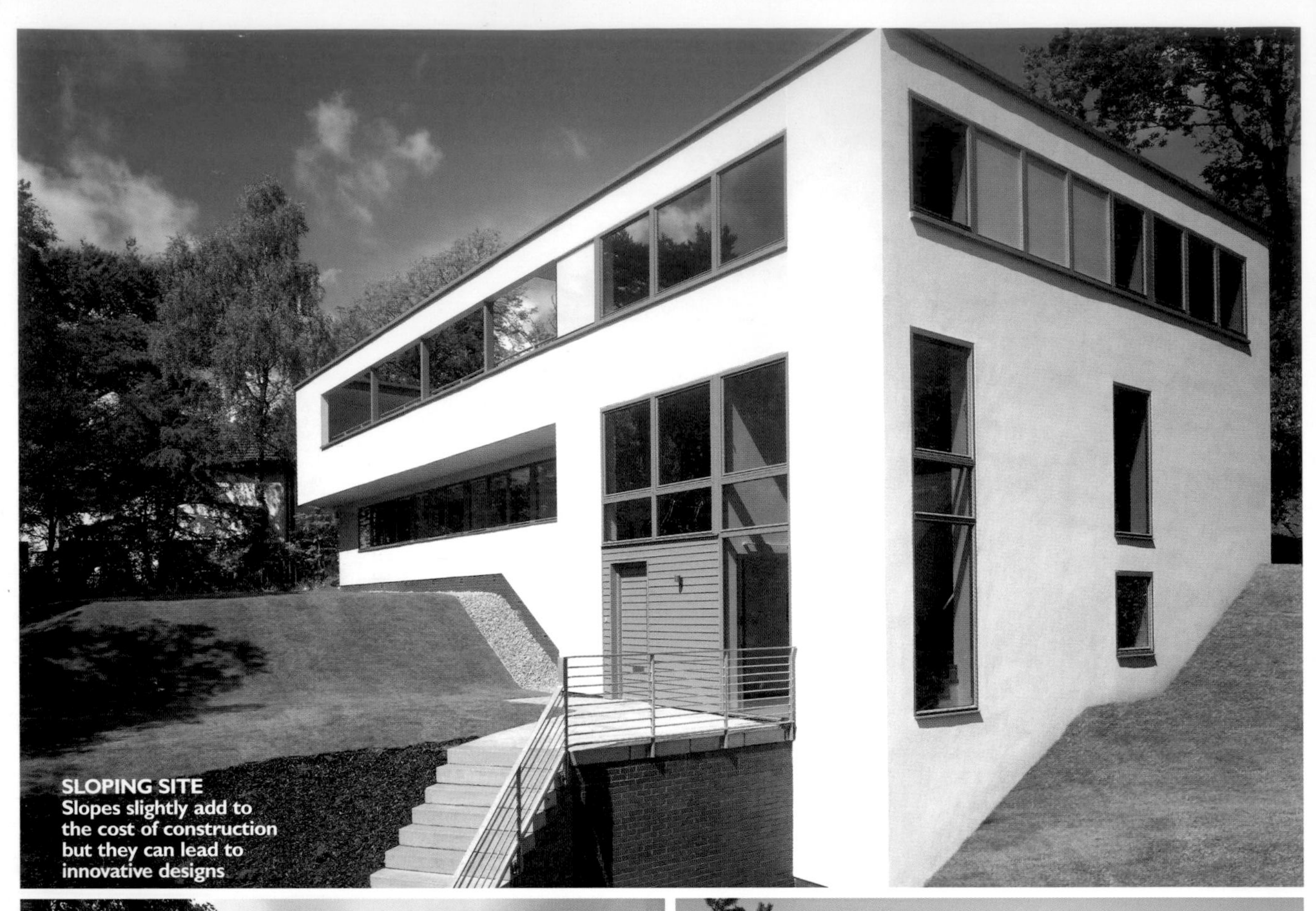

**SLOPING SITE**
Slopes slightly add to the cost of construction but they can lead to innovative designs

**INNER CITY**
It's possible to find small, awkward sites in the middle of cities, perhaps currently used by garages or small units, for instance.

**WOODLAND**
It's possible to replace existing houses in the countryside but only rarely can you get permission to build a brand new dwelling on 'virgin' land

**RIVERSIDE**
Whilst building by the river raises issues around flooding, good design can create truly amazing homes

PART ONE

# HOW TO GET YOUR *self-build* STARTED

## *How to find, assess and buy a plot*

So you've decided that self-building is for you. You've understood that building your own home is something anyone can do and the benefits, both in terms of creating a home built for your unique needs as well as the financial rewards, mean that this a project that is well worth undertaking.

Along the way, of course, you'll find plenty of reasons to give up. The results are so huge because, in part, this is something out of the ordinary. There are many hurdles along the way but by far the biggest barrier to success is also, as it happens, the first. Finding a suitable building plot rarely comes easy, unless you're lucky enough to already own your own plot (you might be able to build in your own large garden, should you wish). For many, the search is long and relentless and ultimately unsuccessful.

Let's make one thing clear – if you're spending too much time looking for a building plot, then you're doing something wrong, and almost certainly looking for something you're never going to find. While some of the ways in which you'll find a plot are similar to the processes you'll go through when looking for a house, others are very different.

The first thing you need to do is to define an area in which to look. Now conventional wisdom would have it that the bigger the area you are looking in, the greater the chance you have of finding something – cast a wide net, and so on. There are of course likely to be more building plots that fall within consideration this way, but it's also true that finding a suitable plot can require a degree of intensive research – something that's difficult to carry out over a large area. Location is likely to be defined by work, school and family commitments – bear in mind that plots within an area may vary significantly by price in just the same way that houses do (i.e. individual street locations can have a huge impact on resale value).

CASE STUDY

REPLACEMENT DWELLING

## OAK-FRAME BARN-STYLE

Steve and Sharon Hunt, with their children Harriet and Harvey, had spent years improving their bungalow, situated in a charming wooded 3.5 acre site in Hampshire. But when they were frustrated in their search for a barn to convert, Steve came up with the radical idea of knocking it down and building a new home in its place. "Sharon thought I was mad," says Steve. They went through with their plan, however, and have created an oak-framed home that has a barn-like feel inside and sits beautifully on the tranquil plot.

Unable to find a barn to convert the Hunt's decided to knock down their bungalow and build this barn-style replacement home

## ESTATE AGENTS

Not all estate agents are going to have details of building plots. Although most estate agents are listed on property portal sites such as Rightmove (who even have a 'land' category) and Globrix, not all estate agents advertise on them (it can cost them £100s per branch, per month) and so to be sure you're covering all the agents selling land in your area, register with them all. Picking up the property section of the free weekly newspaper is a good start in order to get a feel for which agents are likely to have land. They tend to be the agents who will deal with larger country properties, agricultural and equestrian opportunities. Not all of the plots for sale in your immediate area are also going to be sold by agents in your area; the regional offices of the large national country homes chains (such as Knight Frank and Savills) might advertise the occasional plot in their regional office that might be dozens of miles from the village that the plot is in.

Half the building plots that come on to the market are for sale through auctions. You should therefore establish the handful of auction houses in your area who hold regular property/land auctions and ensure you get information from them.

Such is the relative scarcity of building plots that any plot advertised for sale is likely to be relatively sought-after. It very much depends on the local housing market – over the past two to three years vendors have had to advertise building plots more and more and be more competitive with pricing in order to get a sale. In large part this is because the self-builder's traditional competitor for a plot – the developer – has steered clear of investing.

## PLOTFINDER

Plotfinder.net is a specialist subscription-based landfinding service that holds a database of the huge majority of building plots and renovation opportunities for sale in the UK. It essentially bypasses the need to scour all the estate agents – details are checked regularly to make sure they are up to date and, crucially, the site also holds details of plots being sold by private individuals (the site is funded by plotfinders rather than charging vendors to advertise). These private sales are particularly valuable because they are unlikely to appear elsewhere – the vendors obviously avoid having to pay estate agents' fees – and are usually worth the subscription (around £40 a year or so) alone. There is no guarantee that you'll find your plot via the site, but it will give you a lot of information on plot prices in the areas you're looking in and, of course, who the

**BUILDING PLOT**

### WHAT AM I LOOKING FOR?

**You can't just build a house on any old bit of land. If that was the case no-one would have any problem finding a plot – indeed the lack of planning laws before 1947 explains why there are so many houses scattered around the countryside. A bit of land becomes a building plot when it has planning permission to build a house on it – so always make sure you're only looking at land with planning permission. It's also worth noting that many people end up replacing an existing house with a new one – so called replacement dwellings. Many estate agents won't necessarily mark these up as potential building plots – more often they are classed as properties in need of refurbishment – and so you'll need to look out for these too.**

local estate agents are who are dealing in land.

Relying on plots that are on the open market might work, but many self-builders find plots in other ways.

## REPLACEMENT DWELLINGS

Every house you see is nothing more than the temporary occupant of a building plot. When you begin to take this view you realise that many houses not marketed as anything other than houses might indeed offer development potential. Of course, this is the route that controversial developers take – they might buy a large house with the intention of replacing it with an apartment block, for instance. They realise that some houses leave their plots under-developed. A small bungalow on a large site is a great example of the kind of thing you could be looking for, but consider too houses that estate agents market as having potential for extension or refurbishment. Their reduced price might make them viable as building plots.

*A small bungalow on a large site is a great example of the kind of thing to look for, but consider too houses that estate agents market as having potential for extension*

Under the current planning laws there is a general presumption that allows any existing house to be replaced on a like-for-like basis, whether it is in a built-up area or in the open countryside. Each local authority has different guidelines, however, on the extent to which you can replace the existing house/bungalow with something bigger. Ideally you don't want to be limited to the existing floor area (making the whole exercise pointless if it's a small cottage you're replacing) and most local authorities will permit some form of 'extension' – perhaps 20% additional floor area, or 20% additional volume. Note that it's not just the amount of 'extension' that's permitted – it's the type. There's a huge difference between 20% extra floor area and 20% extra volume. There are some clever ways to maximise this allowance – the realm of designers and planning consultants – but in general, your local planning authority's guidance is critical to the viability of your project. You can check the policies at your local library or on the planning/development section of the local authority's website (usually it's in a document called the Local Development Plan or Framework).

**REPLACEMENT**

### THE COST OF DEMOLITION

**Demolishing an existing house is much easier and cheaper than many people think. It takes a matter of days and should cost no more than £5-10,000. These costs can be massively decreased (even to zero) by either re-using existing materials or selling them on to minimise the amount of waste you will have to dispose of from the site. Depending on the construction of the original house it can be simply a ball-breaker job. If you're keen to reclaim the bricks, roof tiles and so on, it can be a more artful process – but either way, it is certainly not something that should put you off the idea of replacement.**

## YOU ALREADY OWN IT

A large number of self-builders begin to look for a plot only to realise that it has been right there under their noses all the time. While a few decide to take the radical step of knocking down their existing home, most come to the realisation that their large side or back garden would be the perfect place to build their dream home. This approach has several advantages – not least because it's free (of tax, too – assuming the whole plot is less than half a hectare) – but also because it enables you to enjoy the benefit of living next door to the site while construction takes place. Under current planning laws gardens are classed as previously-developed (brownfield) land and therefore there is an assumption that development can take place, subject to approval of the design and size of the new building. This so-called 'garden-grabbing' is another tactic favoured by developers and it's often hugely controversial locally, as they often want to build large apartment blocks. Perversely, many local planning policies actually encourage apartment building as they set high density targets for land (i.e. the amount of 'units' per hectare) but others, possibly to avoid such controversy, are happy to see one-off homes on gardens. As you own the garden already, time is on your side to allow you to maximise the planning potential.

CASE STUDY

REPLACEMENT DWELLING

## CONTEMPORARY LIVING

**Martin and Helen Hart bought an old cottage on a 1.75 acre woodland site in Kent safe in the knowledge that the planners would allow it to be replaced with a new house, with the scale of it to be negotiated. Incorporating a basement level to maximise their useable living space but minimise the external impact, the plans sailed through and the couple now live in a contemporary style five bedroom home.**

A large feature window allows plenty of natural light into the open plan kitchen and dining area

CASE STUDY

BUILT IN THE GARDEN

## QUALITY CONTEMPORARY DESIGN

**When Julian and Erika bond moved into a large stone house in their pretty Dorset village they had no idea that 10 years later they would be living in a self-built ultra-contemporary home in the garden. The plot was long and thin but the aptly named Half-Moon House with its sweeping curves has made stunning use of the space to create a comfortable, interesting and airy home for their retirement.**

The central 'drum is home to the 12ft long burr elm table which they've owed for 30 years

## GARDENS

A huge number of self-built plots are formed from the side and rear gardens of existing houses. This is a two-pronged approach with the first part (identifying potential plots) being much easier than the second (convincing the owner to sell it to you.)

Firstly, you need to identify gardens that offer development potential – and it's here where concentrating on a particular village or part of town begins to make sense, as this can be a fairly time-consuming process. You can identify plots by walking or driving around but you're much better with an aerial view and to that end using Ordnance Survey SiteMaps (which give defined outlines of buildings and plots on one of three defined scales) and/or Google Maps is a great way to get a picture of potential plots that might be hidden behind hedges and trees. What you're looking for is a large garden in a row of houses that looks like it could easily accommodate a house – preferably to the side (with street frontage) but possibly to the rear (where access will usually be on the same driveway as that serving the existing house).

If there doesn't appear to be any large side gardens in your area, then you could consider the old developer trick of patching together existing gardens – perhaps cutting the back 15 metres off three long gardens and creating an access from a side road. This is hugely difficult to pull off – you're negotiating with three parties and you can guarantee not everyone will be terribly accommodating – and can take years, but it is another route.

Secondly, you need to approach the owner. Although you can make a planning application for your dream home on any old garden you've identified – you don't have to own a piece of land in order to apply for planning permission on it – it's a pointless exercise unless you're the person who is going to benefit from that permission (and subsequent uplift in value). Chances are that the owner of said large garden has always considered it to be an asset in financial terms – gardens per se are worth more than agricultural land (which tends to be valued at around £3-5,000 an acre) but not as much as land that already has planning permission for a house on it. You need to approach the owner with a proposal that will pay the full market value for the piece of land as it would be with planning permission on it, but ensuring you are the purchaser. This is called an 'option agreement' and is a legal document – it will need to be drafted by your solicitors – that says, subject to you gaining planning permission, you agree to pay a certain amount and the owners agree to sell to you.

This approach can be frustrating. Nine times out of ten the owners will say no. Ideally you would drop a letter through the front door and, if there's no response, follow it up a week or two later with a personal visit. You really have nothing to lose (apart from a bit of pride) but the key, no matter what the rejection you get, is to leave some form of contact for them. Most homeowners with large gardens will already have plans for what they want to do with them – usually leave it to a family member, or in most instances leave it as a large garden – but plans do change. People get older and find a large garden goes from being a benefit to a burden. They might need the windfall within months of your visit. You never know unless you ask.

*People get older and find a large garden goes from being a benefit to a burden. They might need the windfall within a few months of your visit. You never know unless you ask.*

As a self-builder you do have one key advantage in this situation – they know what they're getting, and there is an element of control. If they decide they want to sell off the garden as a building plot one day on the open market they have little control over who their new neighbours are going to be. The new owner could even be a developer who wants to build a large apartment block. By selling to you (and by you presenting yourself as a charming, quiet family) they can realise their asset without upsetting the status quo (and the rest of the street) too much. You could even present yourself as happy to build something that meets with their approval.

**ACCESS**

### RANSOM STRIPS

**One of the keys to making a potential building plot viable is to ensure it has an acceptable access from the highway. You should be able to access the plot without having to cross private land – which is why some people own so-called 'ransom strips', which are small strips of land that block off a plot from being accessed. One of the fundamental checks in the conveyancing process when buying land is to ensure it has access to the highway. Local authority highways departments are also consulted on access in the planning process.**

## OLD UTILITY LAND

Many of the former large public utility companies (water, electrics, railways, and so on) still have large stocks of land that might be attractive to self-builders. It isn't necessarily quite as it sounds – railway land isn't always next to a railway, for instance – and many companies are being encouraged to dispose of their assets, some of which would have development potential. In the case of the former utilities, large plots that housed large substations are now no longer required and could prove to be excellent plots in otherwise built-up areas. You'll need to track down the Estates Departments of the companies, many of whom dispose of land through the national auction houses.

## COLLECTIVE LAND PURCHASES

As mentioned above, many old houses or big plots are perfect for creating more than one unit – in many cases they are out of the financial reach of the individual self-builder. However, getting together as a group and pooling your financial resources all of a sudden gives you the buying power to go after those larger houses to turn into a mini-development of two or three plots.

# *What to Consider When You're Looking at a Plot*

There are many factors to consider when you go to see a building plot. It's a huge investment and of all the influencing factors the viability of the site will have the biggest impact on your enjoyment of the finished house. You need to treat a visit to a plot as a way to survey all of the key issues. Here are the main things to consider.

*There isn't anything that will stop a house being built. There is a solution to every potential problem – but that solution might cost more than the standard.*

## PRICE

The number one question that plotfinders always ask about plots is, "is it the right price?" The vendor or a local estate agent will be able to give you the approximate value of the finished house on that land in that specific location. You need to subtract the estimated building costs of the finished house (more on which later, but estimate around £1,000/m²) and another 10-20% as your developer's profit (which will also be a helpful contingency if things go wrong). What you're left with is the true value of the plot, which will hopefully be the same or preferably more than you're intending to pay.

## THE IMMEDIATE VICINITY

Your assessment will begin before you get to the plot and even before you get in the car. Check out the site using Google Maps and Street View and get a feel for the area – both in terms of its scenery and views but more importantly the local architecture – which may well have an effect on the type of house you'll end up building.

Pre-preparing in this way enables you to ask the key questions on site during the visit rather than afterwards. Is there a likelihood that the plot is sloping? Are there big trees on the site? Also, is this really an area where you want to live – after all, it's one thing you can't change.

You'll also want to spend time before your visit checking average house prices, recent houses on the market on the same street, and key facilities like schools and shops.

**Despite recent changes to planning policies, gardens can still be a good source of building land**

## GROUND CONDITIONS

Ground conditions do vary according to both the geological make-up of the area (some areas have more clay than others, some are built on rock, etc) and the individual site (particularly if formed in former gardens, the top level of the plot might well be made-up ground such as top soil, that can't be used to build a house off.) Try and get an idea of the ground condition itself by physically inspecting it. You could also put a call into the local building inspector – usually they are more than happy to offer informal advice over the phone on the understanding that it is not binding. In truth there isn't anything that will stop a house being built. There is a solution to every potential problem – but of course that solution might cost more than the standard.

## BOUNDARIES

Are the boundaries of the site clearly defined and do they match the siteplan that should form part of the agent's details? You need to be clear as to exactly what land you are buying. Ideally the boundaries would be clearly defined by hedges, walls or fences. Who owns this fences and walls? If there is security fencing on site, is it hired

CASE STUDY

INFILL PLOTS

## OAK-FRAME SUCCESS

**Merry and Ben Albright's compact plot, which was formerly used as a breakers' yard, had planning permission for a large two-storey property with the proviso that the an ugly air-raid shelter in the middle of the plot was retained. "We simply couldn't afford to build the approved design, but the planners were happy with our smaller, cottage," says Ben. "In the end, though, the position of the shelter meant that we couldn't comply with council demands to provide three parking spaces and a turning space. Our planning officer then suggested demolishing the shelter, so that we were able to relocate the house and have room to comply with the planning conditions."**

The new oak frame home sits on a plot that housed an old air-raid shelter

or bought, and if so, at what cost? How mature are the hedges and will they provide sufficient privacy?

## ACCESS

You need to get an idea of where the driveway will go and where cars will be parked. Does the site have direct, unobstructed access to the road and does it affect you idea of where the house should be positioned?

## NEIGHBOURS AND OVERLOOKING

Use the time at the site to have a look at what's next door. Get an idea of who your potential neighbours are going to be and what type and size of house they have. Will there be an issue of overlooking into your back garden? Will your new house affect their privacy?

## ORIENTATION

Ideally a rear garden should face south, in order to enjoy sun throughout the day. The orientation might be something you can change at the planning stage although it's often difficult to change it completely from the approved plans.

## TRAFFIC NOISE

How close is the plot to the road and, if it's close, is the road going to prove a problem? Traffic noise needn't affect the inside of a house thanks to modern building techniques and double/triple glazing, but it can have an impact on how serene (or otherwise) the garden is. If you're visiting the plot at the weekends or after work, try and visit again during rush hour. Traffic noise can also affect the internal floorplan – placing the master bedroom at the loudest part of the plot is not the best idea.

## SERVICES

You will need to provide water, electricity, telephone and probably gas to your new house, and connect to the sewer system. Many rural sites will be too far away from the gas main to make connection a realistic possibility, and as a result the conventional alternative is to buy in oil or LPG. However, you could also consider renewable

energy generation such as a ground source heat pump or solar panels. You should always check the estimated cost of connecting to these key services before purchasing – even going as far as getting potential quotes before purchasing.

The provision of services in place is a key benefit of buying a 'serviced' plot or an existing house to demolish. Expect to pay in the region of £5-10,000 in order to gain connection to the key services – it all depends on how far away you are from the mains.

## THE EXISTING PLANNING PERMISSION

The site you're looking at should have planning approval on which to build a house of the approximate size that would appeal to you. Some important points on this. Firstly, check that the planning permission is in date. Planning permissions last a minimum of three years and a maximum of five (it depends on when they were granted and it will say on the planning permission approval document). Make sure that there is enough time left in the planning

**SMALL WONDER**
**When a small plot came up for sale next to the cottage in which they had lived for years, Ian and Sarah Gluyas leapt at the chance. They had been looking to stay in the village and self-building proved the best way forward. "It was a gamble:as the site came with permission and plans for a three bed detached house little bigger than the one we had been living in." Working with a designer they managed to get the extra bedroom they needed.**

permission for you to commence work without having to reapply – don't assume that you'll be able to renew the planning approval, as local policies change all the time.

Secondly, have a good look at the approved plans. It's important to understand that you can apply for permission to build a different house – based on a design that you have come up with – without jeopardising the existing approval. In theory you can apply dozens of times and gain dozens of different approvals on the same site, and you can build any of them. However, you will need to investigate the planning situation more closely if the approved plans are radically different to what you intend to build – particularly if it's a single storey design and you want a regular house. Ask the agents why there is only permission for a bungalow. In many cases vendors applying for permission on a plot to add to its value before selling it off will apply for the least controversial scheme possible (a bungalow). There would in many instances be nothing to stop you successfully applying for a two-storey house. Take a view of the neighbouring properties at this stage – if it is a neighbourhood of bungalows, you might face more of a battle.

## THE PLOT'S SIZE

In the first section we explained the size of building plots and what they mean in reality. You should spend time at the visit getting an idea of where the house will go and what size garden and driveway this will give you. If the position of the house is not pegged out you could make some rudimentary markers by walking out the dimensions – or by bringing along a measure.

## LEVELS

A full levels survey is beyond your scope but you will want to get an idea of the lie of the land. Slopes put many people off potential building plots but while they can add a few thousand pounds to the cost, they are not usually sufficient to make a housebuilding project completely unviable. In many cases they can actually provide the impetus for a more interesting one-off design, perhaps taking advantage of views, or the provision of a semi-basement.

# The Buying Process

## PRIVATE TREATY

Many plots are for sale by private treaty, in much the same way that regular houses are. If you were interested in a plot that was for sale in this way you would a) make an acceptable offer; b) carry out legal checks through the conveyancing process; c) exchange contracts and complete the sale.

It is imperative that before you make an offer you should have the finance in place. You will need a mortgage agreement in principle or other means. As there is often a lot of competition for building plots, buyers who can move quickly will be in prime position – owners of plots are unlikely to be happy to wait for you to sell your own and be part of a regular chain. As a result, many plotfinders decide they need to commit to selling their own house and moving into rented accommodation – with cash/finance ready to go – before seriously looking for a plot.

*Make sure you set an upper limit before you start bidding. Also, you'll need to have the finance in place in order to complete any successful bid before you start*

## AUCTION

A large number of building plots are offered for sale through auction. Buying at auction can be a daunting process for the unitiated. Here's the best approach:

Do your research beforehand.

The days after the gavel falls on your successful bid is not the time to begin further investigation – the successful bid forms the binding contract in the auction

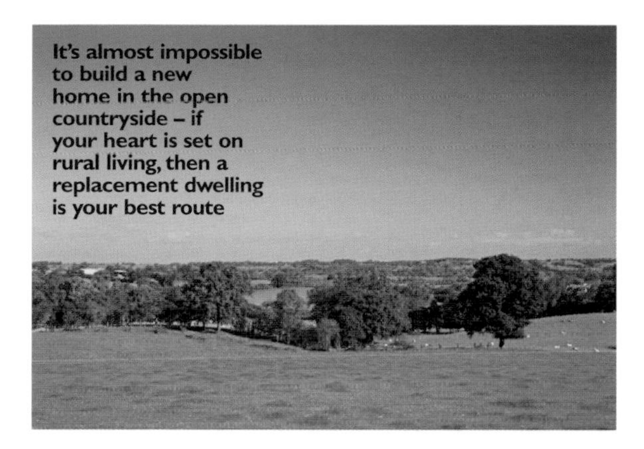
It's almost impossible to build a new home in the open countryside – if your heart is set on rural living, then a replacement dwelling is your best route

As soon as you buy your site, make sure it gets secured with security fencing (best to buy it if you intend to keep it for more than three or four months)

process and you are expected to complete the sale within 28 days, or you'll lose your deposit (which tends to be 10% of the sale price). So you need to do your investigations before you bid. Most auctioneers will have a copy of all the relevant and necessary legal documents in their offices which you won't be able to take away but you will be able to examine. If you're serious about the plot, it might be wise to talk to a conveyancing solicitor beforehand to find out what you'll need to look for. The key factors are obviously relevant and current planning permission, confirmation of the ownership of the site, and the extent of it, from the Land Registry, local searches pertaining to any restrictions on the site, in addition to evidence of any easements or wayleaves (effectively rights that grant central services, such as sewers, access through or over the property) and covenants on the deeds, which would restrict development in some way. In truth, it is best to copy anything of relevance and show them to your professional adviser. All of this is usually carried out after an offer in a conventional plot buying process – in an auction, you'll need to get it cleared before.

## TACTICS

To get a feel for what the auction will be like, visit a few auctions beforehand. The more experience you have, the more at ease you will feel. When you enter the room, try and get a position at the back of the hall, preferably standing up – so you can see the whole of the room and note anyone bidding on the same lot. Don't jump straight in with a bid – wait to see how things develop and don't be too enthused by a slow start. Things will probably quickly pick up and you will need to play a game that involves some element of brinkmanship if you're to be successful.

Buying Simple advice, but make sure you set an upper limit – you will need to establish what the plot is worth before you start bidding. Also, you'll need to have the finance in place in order to complete any successful bid before you start – so check with your lender before you attend. Also, if you are successful, you'll need to be able to fund a 10% (+ VAT) deposit there and then (some auction houses have different deposit requirements, so check beforehand). Most auction houses accept cheques.

## WHAT HAPPENS WHEN YOU'VE BOUGHT IT?

The first thing you'd want to do once you take ownership of a building plot is to secure it – if you need security fencing it's best to buy it as rental costs add up quickly – and, most importantly, get some insurance to cover the site for public liability, in case of children injuring themselves on the site or some other hazard. There are a range of specialist self-build insurance companies who will offer this facility. It's then a question of working up a design.

**AUCTIONS**

### THE KEY NATIONAL PROPERTY AUCTION HOUSES

**Many local agents carry out property auctions, but there are a couple of national houses that sell hundreds of lots at a time – it's well worth registering for their email alerts.**

- **Pugh & Co: www.pugh-company.co.uk**
- **Allsop: www.allsop.co.uk**

# PART TWO

# THE *Planning* PROCESS AN OVERVIEW

Without satisfactory planning permission, a building plot is not a plot. The key, therefore, is to make sure that you have done all of the research in planning terms before you complete the purchase of your plot. The things to look out for are:

## PERMISSION IN PLACE AND CURRENT

The plot has planning permission to build a house of a size and shape similar to the one you would like to build (it doesn't have to be identical – more of which later) and that the planning permission is current (they expire after three or five years depending on when they were granted – it should say on the actual approval document when it expires). Do not assume that a planning permission that has expired can be easily renewed – policies change and what was acceptable then might not be now.

## CHECK THE CONDITIONS

All planning approvals come with a list of permissions. In many cases they are straightforward to meet – they may ask for the parking arrangements to be delivered first of all, or for final approval on the brick choice – but in some cases they can be pretty onerous to meet. For instance they might ask for approval over every aspect of the exterior look (down to colour of the window frames and particular roof tiles) or they might stipulate that the house not be built within a certain distance of a protected tree on the site, and so on. It's important to check through the conditions on the existing planning document – because even if you don't intend to built to the approved plans, they might give you clues as to what the key restrictions on the site are.

## CHECK THE PLANNING HISTORY

Most local councils now publish the full details of a planning application on their websites (and if not, they will be available at the local council offices or library). These applications – searchable by planning reference number (which the agent should be able to give you) or address – are a hugely useful resource for the potential plot purchaser as they not only give the usual set of plans and approval documents but they collate submissions and all correspondence. The key is that they show how difficult it was for the owners to get planning approval.

Planners are less concerned with the way a house looks away from the street frontage, so many self-builders are more radical with their rear elevations

# CHANGING EXISTING APPROVAL

## *Get want you want*

Once given, planning approvals cannot be taken back and, crucially, any one plot can have limitless numbers of planning approvals on it. So permission could in theory be granted on the same site to build a big Georgian house, a modern white render bungalow, and so on. The self-builder can enact any of the existing planning approvals and ignore the rest as they wish.

What this means is that the home on the existing plans you will see when you consider buying the plot is not (necessarily) the one you will end up having to build. You may well love it, in which case you can simply go ahead – but the chances are that you will want to make at the very least minor amendments and more probably build a completely different house.

*Plots owners looking to get planning permission will put in an application for the least controversial, small house they can simply to make their bit of land more valuable.*

## MAKING SMALL AMENDMENTS TO AN APPROVED PLAN

It's possible within the planning system to make so-called 'minor amendments' to an already-approved planning permission without needing to make a new planning application. Planning officers can, under their 'delegated' powers (meaning powers that they have to make final decisions without reference to further interested parties) consider whether an amendment is indeed minor or large enough to require further consultation in the form of a full planning application.

**CHANGES THAT ARE ACCEPTABLE AS MINOR AMENDMENTS INCLUDE:**

- minor 'elevational' changes to a house design (such as window sizes and positions, the introduction of a chimney, etc) that don't impact on neighbours
- an extension to the plan that is not nearer to a neighbour

**MORE SIGNIFICANT CHANGES THAT WILL REQUIRE A NEW PLANNING APPLICATION INCLUDE:**

- making the house bigger and/or closer to neighbours
- radical changes to the design, such as a change in the cladding (e.g. from brick to render or wood cladding).

Ultimately this is a bit of a grey area and the best course of action is to call your local planning office with details of your intended changes. They will then give you guidance as to whether you need to submit a new planning application. It makes sense where possible to contain your changes to the minor amendments area as a new planning application might throw up many more issues. Expect to pay a small fee of £25 for a minor amendment application.

*Ultimately this is a bit of a grey area and the best course of action is to call your local planning office with details of your intended changes.*

## BUILDING A COMPLETELY DIFFERENT HOME

Chances are that you will want to build something completely different to the home that the site has been granted approval for. There are two key things to consider here:

- is the house that you have in your head relevant for this site? It's possible that the dream home you have been carrying around is not suitable for this particular plot. The plot may have different views from a different elevation than what you've already considered; it might also be the case that the surrounding area has more of an impact on what you should be building than you had

CASE STUDY

REPLACEMENT DWELLING

## AN EGLISHMAN''S HOME . . .

**John and Jo Mew's self-build project is one of the best known in the UK. John and Jo bought an old worker's cottage in Sussex with acres of land and, having demolished it, spent the best part of ten years building a brand an extraordinary new mediaeval style castle, complete with moat, in its place.**

It looks anything but a new house, but John and Jo Mew's home in Sussex is in fact a brand new castle

previously imagined. There might be issues around neighbours that you don't want to overlook or trees on the site that you don't want to (or can't) knock down. All of these factors and more might mean that the dream home in your head that you're intending to build here becomes a shoe-horned concept that is best left until next time. Or, if you're so set on building what's in your head, it might be best to move on.

*Buying a plot that doesn't have planning for exactly what you want (but does have planning approval for a house of another type) is less of a risk than you might initially think*

• is there a realistic chance of getting planning for what you want? The planning history of the site is key in this instance. To an extent, buying a plot that doesn't have planning for exactly what you want (but does have planning approval for a house of another type) is less of a risk than you might initially think – after all, you can always sell on the plot again quickly with only minor financial penalty. Some people spend years battling on to get planning permission for the exact house they want to build; for others it's easy and takes a matter of weeks; and for others, it never happens and they end up either building something completely different or selling up and trying elsewhere. How your particular situation will pan out depends entirely on the planning story behind your particular plot – which is why you need to carry out your research beforehand.

*Look for local precedents and sound out the planning office. The more radical your scheme (e.g. modern white house in a Georgian town) the more controversial*

Your chances of getting planning permission for a home that is radically different to what has been approved are greater if the new scheme isn't significantly greater in terms of floor area than what has been approved. Planners are often much more interested in size and volume – the ridge height and footprint – than the details of the design itself (as are neighbours, on the whole) and, if you do want something significantly bigger, it's important to come up a design that reduces its impact. One way to do this would be to have a more complicated roofline and single story aspects of the elevations.

If you want to change an approved bungalow into a two storey house, then the key to understanding whether your scheme is going to be a success or not is to look at the immediate surrounds. Is there a mix of bungalows and two-storey houses? If all of the neighbours are bungalows then it is unlikely that a two-storey house will be acceptable. You might, however, be able to get away with a dormer bungalow, which will give you many of the benefits of a two-storey house without the ridge-height issues of a two storey home. Bear in mind, however, that many owners of plots looking to get planning permission will put in an application for the least controversial, small house they can simply in order to get the approval that makes their bit of land so much more valuable. You as owner and eventual builder will not want to be this conservative and in many cases your plans will be acceptable.

If you don't like the way the approved house design looks – and, after all, few plot vendors invest huge amounts in a design that they will not themselves benefit from – then the chances of you changing it are pretty good, depending on how radical the changes are, the nature of the local area, and the attitude of the planning office. Again, have a look for local precedents and sound out the planning office to get some informal advice. Clearly, the more radical your scheme (e.g. modern white house in a Georgian town) the more controversial the new application; but planning officers aren't necessarily as conservative as you might think.

**PLANNING**

## THE PLANNING COMMITTEE

**If you're not lucky enough to have your planning application decided under the delegated powers of a planning officer, then it will be decided by the local planning committee. The committee is a special group of local councillors who sit in session every few weeks (depending on the size of the council and workload). You will be able to make a speech in support of your claim and the committee will consider all relevant views and make a decision based on the representations they receive. They may or may not take part in a site visit.**

# The Planning Process

**1** You will work with a designer to come up with a scheme that meets your requirements and that you want to build. Ideally you would have already engaged with the local planning office in order to incorporate their comments into the scheme (assuming your planning office is willing to provide constructive comments). Otherwise you should have taken into account the planning history of the site, in addition to local precedents.

**2** You'll make a full planning application. You will need to complete the planning application form (called 1APP and downloadable from your local authority planning department website); submit a siteplan (available from Ordnance Survey); submit the design drawings (both floorplan and elevations); a fee (currently £335); and a design and access statement (an accompanying page or two that summarises the reasoning behind the scheme).

**3** You will then receive an acknowledgement of the council's receipt of the planning application. It will then be publicised on the council's website in their weekly list of applications and neighbours will be informed of the application and invited to comment. Other local bodies, such as Highways, will be asked to comment. Depending on the nature of the scheme and the level of local interest, the application will then either be decided on under delegated powers (by a planning officer) or by the local Planning Committee. A decision will then be made – all of this should occur within two months of the submission of the application.

**4** If you are granted approval then you will be sent a formal document outlining the approval and a list of conditions which will need to be met. If the application is refused, then a document will be sent out giving reasons for the refusal.

THE APPLICATION

## WHAT IF MY APPLICATION GETS REFUSED?

**The simple fact is that the vast majority of refusals can be overcome with an adjustment to the planning application – perhaps a change in roofline or size of the house. You need to, with complete objectivity, assess whether the reasons given for the refusal are based in local planning policy (i.e. in contravention of something the council has set out to achieve, such as no new homes in the countryside) or whether it is based more on opinion and something potentially arguable. If it's the former, then a formal appeal is almost certainly a waste of time and money, not to mention a blight on the plot itself. Only one in three appeals are successful.**

**If you want to persist, you should in the first instance contact your local planning office and engage them in a discussion about the key issues. If you do not reach a satisfactory agreement, then you can launch a formal appeal through the Planning Inspectorate – an often long and complex process which will probably involve the use of planning consultants and plenty of representations. One easier and innovative path around this is to use the Householder Appeals Service, part of the planning inspectorate, who aim to minimise the red tape and process decisions within three months.**

**TIP** It's important to keep a check on the progress of your planning application by making a weekly phonecall to the planning office. They will be able to give you an early indication of how it is being viewed and whether refusal is likely. If they indicate refusal is likely, you can at any time withdraw the application – it's much better to do this and resubmit (it's free to resubmit once within 12 months) than have the plot blighted by a refusal, against which all future applications will be judged..

This new eco friendly home in Worcestershire replaced an old cottage. Local planners allowed the new home to be bigger than what was there already

It's easier to get planning permission for more unusual designs in areas less influenced by strong housing styles. This American-style timber-clad home was self-built in Scotland

PLANNING

## SPECIAL LAND DESIGNATIONS

**Whilst the majority of building plots are situated in areas that have no special planning designation, some do – and it can have an impact on how any planning application you make is received. It's important therefore to understand the key terms.**

### Conservation Area

A Conservation Area is an area of a town, city or village that is deemed to have an architectural or historical merit that is worthy of preservation. A classic Conservation Area would be a row of charming Georgian terraced homes or collection of detached Edwardian homes in a leafy suburb. Whilst building a new home in a Conservation Area isn't impossible, any application is given a much greater scrutiny than one in a non-designated area. In the majority of cases, a Conservation Officer from the local council will be able to give advice on the type of development they like to see in order to enhance the area and protect the existing buildings. Usually this means that any new development would have to be 'sensitive' in its approach (meaning that it ties in with the general look and theme) but increasingly, Conservation Areas like new homes to be very contemporary in their look so they don't look to mimic (usually not very well) the true originals. In essence, the standard of design – whether contemporary or traditional – is likely to be required to be much higher than usual.

While in non-designated areas demolition is not a controversial issue, the act of demolition itself in a Conservation Area requires a planning application and is likely to be closely scrutinised.

### National Parks

If the plot you buy is in a National Park, then any application you make will be more closely scrutinised in design terms than a standard application – but there is no pre-judgement against new dwellings per se. The National Parks have their own planning authorities and each off the parks has its own policies and guidelines.

### SSSI – Site of Special Scientific Interest

If the plot is in an SSSI then it has done pretty well to get planning permission of any sort. More likely is that the plot is adjacent to an SSSI, in which case any application will have to address the concerns that any development will impact on it.

# UNDERSTAND THE FACTS
# *Planning FAQs*

## Why can't we get planning to build in the countryside? There are loads of homes out there.

**This is a common complaint and a cause of frustration to potential self-builders. The houses you see in the countryside can be explained as legacies of very different and much more liberal planning regimes. Before the introduction of the Planning Act in 1947 you could build whatever you wanted, wherever you wanted – hence the older houses in attractive isolated settings. Up until the 1980s it was far from impossible in many areas to get permission to build a new home in the countryside but these days it's all but a pipe dream. The only exceptions are where new homes are built in place of old ones, or homes that serve to support an agricultural business.**

It's very rare that new homes can be built in the countryside

Planners like to see designs based around materials that draw from the local environment, such as timber or stone

## Our future neighbours have already told us they are going to object to our self-build plans. What next?

**Well, contrary to popular myth, neighbours don't actually have the final say on planning issues. They are of course consulted on any planning applications that might affect them, but they are part – and only part – of the consideration. In particular, objections that are based on subjectivity not relating to planning matters – e.g. the effect on their house value – will not influence a decision at all. Only issues of overlooking and the physical impact on the enjoyment of their house are taken into account.**

**It's always best to get neighbours on-side before a project starts by talking them through your intentions, but the sad fact is that many future neighbours can't bear to lose the quiet bit of land next door.**

CASE STUDY

SENSITIVE SITE

Modern, but convetional exterior, hides contemporary open-plan living areas

## CONTEMPORARY SELF-BUILD ON A PLOT WITH A PAST

**Aileen and Dave Downie struggled to get planning permission for their contemporary self-built home in York. Although outline planning permission had existed on the plot since the 1930s, the area had since been recognised as a site of archaeological interest – which meant that the Downies had to carry out a study of the history of the land, and to agree to an archaeologist supervising the early stages of the build. The local planners were also concerned about the contemporary design which Aileen and Dave dealt with by pushing the property behind the regular building line and leaving plenty of trees intact.**

## There are parts of the approved plan we want to change. How best do we go about this?

**Don't forget to make full use of your Permitted Development (PD) Rights. These are special allowances for householders under the planning system that enable certain works to be carried out without the need for planning permission. They include, for example, the ability to convert the loft into habitable accommodation provided the roof doesn't change shape; they also include small extensions to the side and rear of the house up to a certain size. So bear in mind that, in many cases, the amendments you want to make don't necessarily have to form part of the planning process – and you should make your planning officer aware of your knowledge of these rights. More details on PD Rights can be found on your local council website or at the Government's planning information service, Planning Portal.**

## What are Reserved Matters?"

**For many years up until 2006 it was possible to make an outline application which merely established, in principle, the concept of development. This usually consisted of a red line drawn around a plot, with the details of the development – such as the visual appearance and size of the new house – to be applied for later as so-called 'reserved matters'. However, since 2006 the minimum requirements for an outline application have become more detailed so that you can no longer not specify things like ridge height as reserved matters. Consequently, most plotowners tend to submit full planning applications from the start.**

## I want to change around the internal layout of the house. Do I need approval?"

**In short, no. The planning system is only concerned with the external appearance of the house and any internal remodelling changes are more likely to come under the remit of the Building Control department, if at all.**

## "I've bought a plot with planning permission attached but, several years on, haven't done anything with it. We're even thinking about changing the scheme around. What should we do?"

**Planning permissions don't last forever – there is a time limit that is set on the approval document. In Wales this is five years but in England and Scotland it was reduced from five to three in 2006. However it is currently possible to extend this up to five years by renewing (which requires a full application fee). One of the best options for plotowners worried about a planning approval expiring is to commence work – once you've started work, it lasts forever. You can commence work by notifying building control and completing some initial foundation work – at the very least digging some foundations and preferably filling them.**

**There is some confusion on this issue because an outline permission (see below) actually lasts for five years, but the details (reserved matters) need to be applied for within two years of outline approval – and they are valid for three years.**

**Planners are concerned exclusively with the external appearance of the new home, and therefore interiors can be exactly as you want**

PART THREE

# COMING UP WITH YOUR *dream* HOME

## *Key Features of a Dream Home*

Your new self-built home is the perfect opportunity to incorporate many of the features you have always dreamed of being able to enjoy. Here are 20 of the key things that people love to include in their homes.

**• Home Cinema • Master Bedroom Suite • Luxury Showers • Family Kitchen • Home Gym • Underfloor Heating • Double Height/Architectural Space • Home office • Granny annexe • Swimming pool • Sauna • Open-plan living • Playroom • Rainwater harvesting • Lighting and audio/video systems • Gallery Landing • Feature Windows • Renewables • Woodburning Stove • Folding/sliding doors**

# The Design Process

Chances are that designing your own individual home, whether it be a brand new house or one that results from significant renovation work, is the number one reason you are attracted to the whole self-build world. First and foremost, above any of the financial or other benefits you'll enjoy, getting an individual home built entirely around what you want and need is at the forefront of almost everyone's mind. House design is an exciting and highly enjoyable process – it's the moment when your distant dreams become focused reality – but it is important to remember that it is also, by far, the most critical element of any project. Bad design is easily the biggest contributing factor to projects that go wrong, while all successful self-build projects start off with a sound, intelligent design.

*Bad design is easily the biggest contributing factor to projects that go wrong, while all successful self-build projects start off with a sound, intelligent design.*

So how do you ensure your project gets off on the right foot? Avid viewers of 'Grand Designs' and similar programmes will be party to endless tales of self-build woe – but the script is remarkably similar. Ambitious self-builders approach an architect who designs a remarkable new house, guaranteed to be the envy of their friends and family; building work commences, only for builders to bring a sense of grim reality to the proceedings, which usually ends up with our ambitious self-builders going way, way over budget (often double), falling out with their architect and emitting a general sense of disenchantment with the whole process.

## THE BUDGET

The conclusion to be drawn from these situations is that the design was never realistically matched to the self-builder's budget. The truth is that for all successful projects, the number one starting point for the design process is money. Work out to the nearest £10,000 what your build budget is (use the calculator on page 132 as a start) and set all of your design choices (from how big a house you can build, to the actual house design, through to choices on the final fixtures and fittings) around this figure. And, of course, make sure you communicate this figure to your designer, and stress your intention to stick to it. Ask how they can be sure that the house can be built to your budget – many will employ a Quantity Surveyor on your behalf to check the viability of your scheme.

## INSPIRATION AND COMING UP WITH YOUR OWN IDEAS

The key for any designer is getting inside the mind of his/her clients and trying to come up with a design which is the realisation of what they have in their head. Some clients are not very good at communicating their desires and are likely to find their initial discussions with a designer to be polarised. It's much better for a designer to see what kind of things their clients imagine in their dream home than for them to have to guess, and for this reason you should be collecting images and keeping them to present to your designer at your first proper meeting.

*The key for any designer is getting inside the mind of his/her clients and trying to come up with a design which is the realisation of what they have in their head.*

Where to get inspiration (and cut outs)

- self-build magazines. Cut out and keep images of both case studies and individual product shots you like.
- houseplan books. Look at how spaces work with each other.
- the internet.
- homes magazines (they concentrate on decorating, but use some great houses as roomsets and show lots of nice fittings and furniture).
- books on individual architects. Research some great designers and see what space they created.
- Showhomes. While much of the design work that goes into developers' housing is limited, walking around showhomes will get you a good idea of spaces in reality and how they relate to dimensions. It will also give you an idea of how to get maximum space out of smaller floor areas.

A good design will incorporate as much of the natural landscape as possible

The idea is not necessarily to create a list of features that your designer should include, but rather to give the designer an impression of the kind of things that you like in design terms (which is why things like kitchens, fittings and furniture are just as important as big spaces). Present this to your designer as a 'mood board' and comment on why you like certain aspects.

## ASSESSING YOUR SITE

Another critical element in your design process is to analyse the plot you are intending to build on. Every plot is unique, not just in its shape and size and slope, but also in its orientation and surroundings. All good designers will know your plot before designing a house for it and you should make them aware of any issues that you think might influence the scheme. While the more obvious ones include slopes and odd sizes and shapes, factors like views, orientation and overlooking will have a critical impact on your design. Do an initial assessment of what you might think works best. Take inspiration from the houses around you and ensure that the house design you come up with is a result on these issues. Some sites may make some design ideas unfeasible; others, for example those with slopes, may make some design ideas (such as upside down living, or basements) much more of design priority. Don't forget too, if finances are an important factor, to consider the end value of the house you intend to build, in terms of style, fittings and number/size of rooms.

## PLANNING

The final external factor that will influence your design will be local planning guidance. While individual local factors are too complex to go into here, you should make an assessment of the immediate neighbours to see what style of house they have been built in, and make an informal initial approach to your local planning department to get a sense of what they might feel is acceptable, and how they react to your initial thoughts.

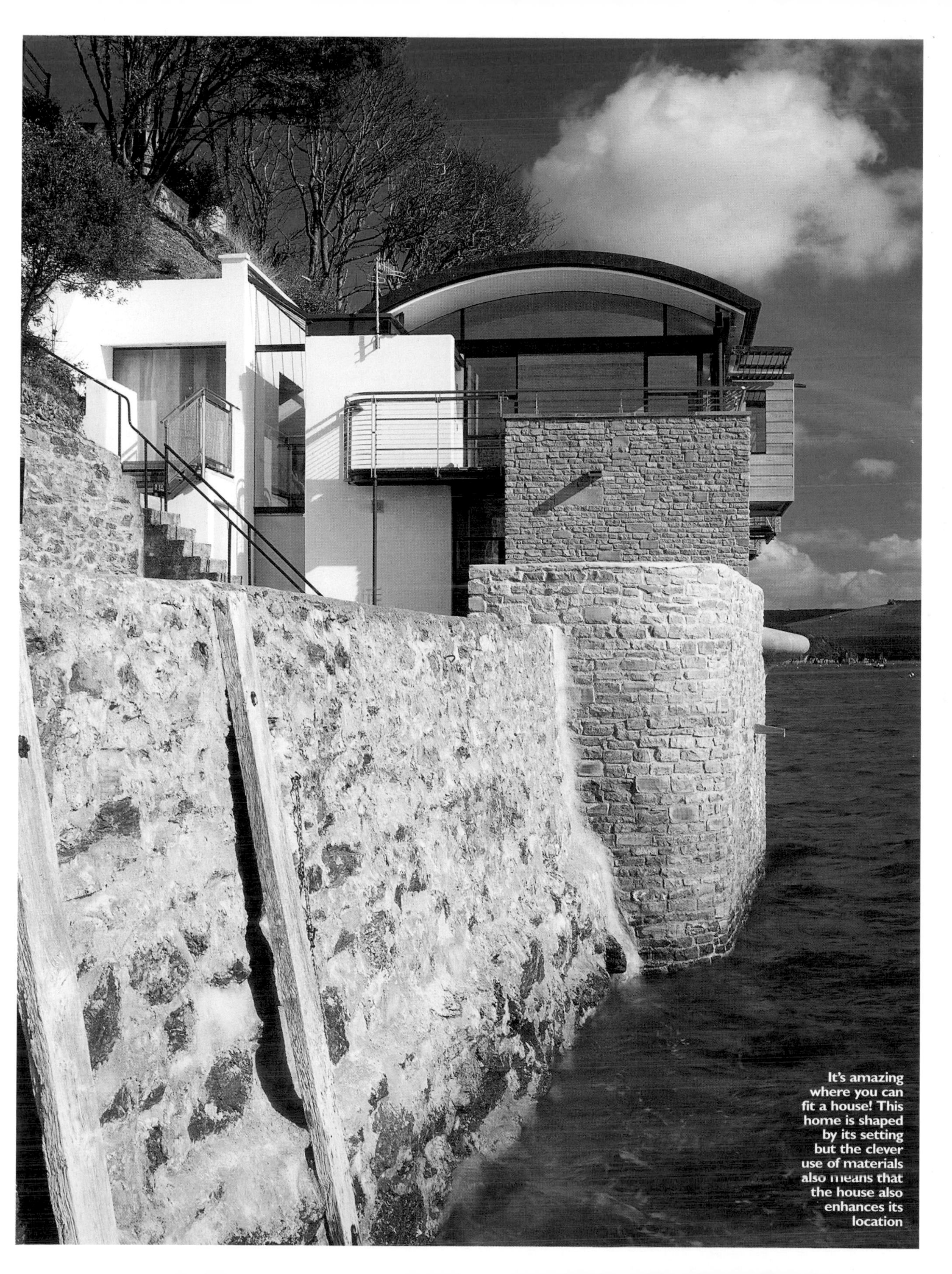

It's amazing where you can fit a house! This home is shaped by its setting but the clever use of materials also means that the house also enhances its location

Architectural statements – such as these fantastic sweeping stairs – are the kind of things that really set off a self-built home

# *Finding a designer*

You can get your new house designed by any one of a number of professionals:

## ARCHITECT

A house designer can only call him/herself an Architect if they have completed the seven years' worth of training to become chartered (and with it gain membership of the Royal Institute of British Architecture, RIBA) and are registered with the Architects Registration Board (ARB). Because not all Architects specialise in one-off housing, you can search the lists at www.architecture.com for house design specialists in your area or, perhaps more easily, contact an organisation called Associated Self-build Architects, a group of Architects who cater specifically for self-builders (www.asba-architects.org). Another option for those carrying out extension or remodelling work who want an innovative solution is to contact Architect Your Home (at www.architect-yourhome.com). Architect's fees vary enormously depending on the individual and fees for a whole project can be anything between £5,000 (for design drawings only from a small practice) up to £50,000 and beyond (for a recognised Architect to provide designs and a supervisory service). Ensure you get an agreement on fees up front and ask to see previous examples of work.

## ARCHITECTURAL TECHNOLOGISTS

A large number of house designers don't go through the process of becoming a Chartered Architect and many of them opt to become technologists instead. The name is slightly misleading, as while many of them do indeed do

Many self-builders like to incorporate outside spaces into the design

Self-building really is about getting anything you want and pushing the boundaries of design – such as this glass floor (be careful when wearing a skirt, ladies)

the nitty-gritty drawing work for Architects, many more act as fully-fledged house designers in every sense of the word. Many self-builders find technologists to be more grounded in budget issues and, in some instances, more approachable than Architects. The group has recently achieved Chartered status itself and a list of members can be found at www.ciat.org.uk

## SURVEYORS

While this type of professional includes everyone from building surveyors to some estate agents, many Chartered Surveyors offer comprehensive design services. A full list can be found at www.rics.org

## OTHER DESIGNERS

Look in an Yellow Pages under 'Architectural Services' and you'll find a collection of loud adverts for local house designers – with names ranging from the solid-sounding through to the rather lively 'Plans People'. Quite distinct from the more austere 'Architects' section, this varied bunch offer a broad range of different qualities, skills and levels of experience. In general terms, they are likely to be cheaper than Architects and some may well be just as talented. There is no vetting process for general house designers – you could set yourself up as one tomorrow if you wish – and so it's essential that you see previous work, ask for proof of insurance and, again, establish fees upfront.

## PACKAGE COMPANIES

All of the package companies offer a design service (as part of an overall materials/labour contract), but the details of what is offered varies from company to company. While almost all of the leading companies have a range of standard designs, they encourage clients to suggest alterations off these basic plans; others offer a standard book of plans with no changes permitted; others offer totally bespoke design services, fresh for every project. Establish which route your chosen company uses. While design is included as part of the overall package, you will of course find it factored in to your overall costs, although many clients find the fact that they are not paying upfront for design services a big bonus of this build route. Another big advantage of using a package company for house design is that they are much more able to link your design to your build costs.

# The Initial Scheme

Having chosen a designer and given them a brief, expect to receive back a first look at your new house on paper within 2-4 weeks. As the designer will make clear, you should look closely at these plans and see how they relate to the brief you have given them. Ask why certain elements have been missed out and others included. Most importantly, check the sizes (and numbers) of rooms to ensure that they are sufficient for your needs. Look at the overall scheme and analyse it carefully, and at the follow-up meeting ensure that all avenues have been fully explored. Finally, confirm estimated build costs with the designer.

Having agreed any amendments, the scheme is now ready to go through the planning process. Once approval is given, your designer will then need to come up with building regulations drawings for approval by the council. Gaining approval on that means work is ready to start on site – but with a well-considered design behind you, the seeds of success have already been sown.

If you want an intricate contemporary design – something different, like this new home – then an architect is your best bet

DESIGN FEES

## WHAT TO PAY

**For a full service – including contract administration and the full 'hand-holding' game, an Architect will charge between 7-10% of the build cost, according to Architect Julian Owen, whereas for a partial service, which might just include the initial design work, they tend to work on an agreed hourly rate, which will depend on the size of the project. RIBA quote between £55-150/hour for design work, and clients would be expecting to pay £5-10,000 for work on this basis. Julian continues: "fees are not that different between Architects and Technologists". CIAT backs this up: "It is a common misconception that CIAT members charge less than architects, but fees will vary from practice to practice." The world of house designers contains a huge disparity in fees. You could easily find someone willing to charge less than £1,000 for plans drawing services; while the more experienced and accomplished designers might well charge as much as an Architect. Whether it's a fixed fee or an hourly rate will usually depend on how much work goes into the scheme (they'll usually put you on an hourly rate if there's lots of negotiation involved.) In general, whoever you go to, you should expect to pay between £5-10,000 for design fees. As mentioned, this may be as low as £1,000, or it may be as high as £50,000 from a leading London firm - Ouch. It's worth noting too that despite the common conception, Architects aren't getting rich out of their work (usually). According to the RIBA Salary Survey 2009, more than a fifth of architects are out of work, and average earnings are £45,000.**

PART FOUR

# A DETAILED GUIDE TO *building* COSTS

## *How Much will my New Home Cost to Build?*

A new home can cost anything to build from £50,000 up to millions of pounds. At which end of the scale your project will be depends on two main factors – the size of the house, and what you put in it (also known as the specification).

As of 2009 the average cost of building a new home for a self-builder was around £210,000. This didn't include the cost of the plot – when we talk about build costs, we exclude the cost of the land. The building world tends to think about costs in terms of reference to size – when you buy flooring, for instance, it costs say £20/m$^2$, and so on. Builders quote in this way, too – it's a way around dealing with the variances in size but comparing the differences in specification. So a builder may quote in a cost per square metre (or if they are a bit more traditional, square foot) – it's often around £1,000/m$^2$ or £100/sqft – and you will need to multiply this by your expected floor area to get a rough early estimate of your build costs.

Local materials were used both inside and out

## COASTAL COTTAGE

The major influence on how much a house will cost to build is, of course, its size. Nicky and Robin van der Bij's newly self-built home in Cornwall, which replaced an old cottage, is super-energy efficient but managed to be built for just £115,000 thanks to it being relatively small (at 100m$^2$ it has three bedrooms) and the couple managing the project themselves (rather than using a builder). In spite of it's stone cladding the cottage is actually a timber frame structure.

The kitchen features bespoke American oak kitchen units

Unusual architectural features such as high-level windows and central feature flues all add to the cost

So how much will your new home cost to build? The bigger the house, the more it will cost. However it's the specification that will have the biggest impact, as the price of building materials and home finishes varies so wildly – a home that's kitted out with state-of-the-art technology, high-quality flooring, top-end windows and handmade bricks will cost well over double the same size house fitted with basic equivalents. Another big factor will be the amount of input you have on the site itself. Paying a main contractor or project manager to co-ordinate all the trades and materials on your behalf will cost you around 10-20% of the overall cost – if you can take on these responsibilities yourself, as many self-builders do, then you'll save in the region of £15-50,000 of the build cost. Many self-builders, regardless of their levels of competency, manage to get involved in some aspect of the physical work on site – whether it is landscaping and decorating or simply labouring for a few days. Anything you can do will save money off your total spend when you consider you'll pay between £80-200 a day for labour.

These factors taken into account, most self-builders spend between £150-300,000 on the cost of their home.

**KEY CALCULATING TOOLS**

## MEASURING FLOOR AREA

There are several different ways of measuring floor area and you need to be sure that you are talking on the same standards as your builder or package supplier. The most common way of measuring floor area is the so called internal floor area, also known as the net floor area. It measures along the inside line of the external walls of the house and includes the space taken up by the internal walls – it also includes all the storeys of the house – so a two storey house would have (almost) double the net floor area of the same house built as a bungalow. The other method, gross floor area, effectively measures to include the outside of the external walls (imagine a tape measure wrapped around the house). Owing to the thickness of external walls, the difference between the two can be pretty significant – an important factor when dealing with European suppliers and package companies, who often speak in gross floor area terms.

**1m² = 10.76 sq ft**
**1 sq ft = 0.0929m²**

**(therefore to turn a sq ft measurement into m², multiply the number by 0.0929)**

CASE STUDY

TRADITIONAL-STYLE HOME

Self-building allows you to create the home you want

Revealing the roof structure has created a dramatic space

## DOUBLE-SIZE FIVE-BED HOME

**Completing much of the work themselves enabled Simon and Sally England to create a fabulous traditional home for just £194,000 – a figure all the more impressive considering the fact that the size of the house, at 325m², is twice that of a regular five bedroom detached home. The Englands used a main contractor and eventually resorted to DIY to save money, tackling jobs such as fitting the bathrooms and kitchen, tiling, painting, laying floors and landscaping.**

# Estimating Your Costs in Detail

## AVERAGE BUILD COST GUIDE

1 Choose your build route: read along the top line. Will you be using a main contractor/package company, some of your own labour, or something in between?

2 Size up your project: look down the left hand column to match the size of your project.

3 Choose your area: there are for costs for each size, delending on where you are building.

4 Choose your build quality: there are also three costs for each quality of finish – from standard/developer to excellent/top end.

| £/m² for gross internal floor area | | BUILD ROUTE A (DIY & SUBCONTACTORS) | | | BUILD ROUTE B (SUBCONTACTORS) | | | BUILD ROUTE C (BUILDER & SUBCONTACTORS) | | | BUILD ROUTE D (MAIN CONTRACTOR) | | |
|---|---|---|---|---|---|---|---|---|---|---|---|---|---|
| | | BUILD QUALITY | | | BUILD QUALITY | | | BUILD QUALITY | | | BUILD QUALITY | | |
| **SINGLE STOREY HOUSES** | | Standard | Good | Excellent | Standard | Good | Excellent | Standard | Good | Excellent | Standard | Good | Excellent |
| SMALL (Up to 90m²) | Greater London | 1029 | 1191 | 1432 | 1090 | 1261 | 1516 | 1150 | 1331 | 1600 | 1211 | 1401 | 1684 |
| | South East | 902 | 1044 | 1256 | 955 | 1106 | 1330 | 1009 | 1167 | 1404 | 1062 | 1229 | 1478 |
| | NW, SW East & Scotland | 821 | 950 | 1143 | 869 | 1006 | 1210 | 917 | 1062 | 1277 | 965 | 1118 | 1344 |
| | Mids, Yorks, NE & Wales | 785 | 909 | 1092 | 831 | 962 | 1157 | 877 | 1015 | 1221 | 923 | 1069 | 1285 |
| MEDIUM (90-160m²) | Greater London | 942 | 1144 | 1486 | 998 | 1211 | 1573 | 1053 | 1278 | 1661 | 1109 | 1345 | 1748 |
| | South East | 827 | 1003 | 1303 | 875 | 1061 | 1380 | 924 | 1120 | 1456 | 973 | 1179 | 1533 |
| | NW, SW East & Scotland | 752 | 913 | 1186 | 796 | 966 | 1256 | 841 | 1020 | 1326 | 885 | 1074 | 1396 |
| | Mids, Yorks, NE & Wales | 719 | 873 | 1134 | 762 | 924 | 1201 | 804 | 975 | 1268 | 846 | 1027 | 1335 |
| LARGE (161m²+) | Greater London | 839 | 1101 | 1381 | 888 | 1165 | 1462 | 938 | 1230 | 1543 | 987 | 1295 | 1624 |
| | South East | 736 | 965 | 1211 | 779 | 1021 | 1282 | 822 | 1078 | 1353 | 866 | 1135 | 1425 |
| | NW, SW East & Scotland | 669 | 878 | 1103 | 709 | 929 | 1168 | 748 | 981 | 1232 | 787 | 1033 | 1297 |
| | Mids, Yorks, NE & Wales | 640 | 840 | 1054 | 677 | 889 | 1116 | 715 | 939 | 1178 | 753 | 988 | 1240 |
| **TWO STOREY HOUSES** | | | | | | | | | | | | | |
| SMALL (90-130m²) | Greater London | 990 | 1146 | 1407 | 1049 | 1213 | 1490 | 1107 | 1280 | 1573 | 1165 | 1348 | 1656 |
| | South East | 869 | 1005 | 1235 | 920 | 1064 | 1307 | 971 | 1123 | 1380 | 1022 | 1182 | 1452 |
| | NW, SW East & Scotland | 790 | 915 | 1124 | 836 | 968 | 1190 | 883 | 1022 | 1256 | 929 | 1076 | 1323 |
| | Mids, Yorks, NE & Wales | 755 | 875 | 1074 | 800 | 926 | 1137 | 844 | 978 | 1200 | 888 | 1029 | 1264 |
| MEDIUM (131-220m²) | Greater London | 834 | 1010 | 1280 | 883 | 1069 | 1356 | 932 | 1128 | 1431 | 981 | 1188 | 1506 |
| | South East | 732 | 886 | 1123 | 775 | 938 | 1189 | 818 | 990 | 1255 | 861 | 1042 | 1321 |
| | NW, SW East & Scotland | 665 | 806 | 1022 | 704 | 854 | 1082 | 744 | 901 | 1142 | 783 | 949 | 1202 |
| | Mids, Yorks, NE & Wales | 637 | 771 | 977 | 674 | 816 | 1034 | 712 | 861 | 1092 | 749 | 907 | 1149 |
| LARGE (221m² +) | Greater London | 770 | 985 | 1237 | 815 | 1043 | 1309 | 860 | 1101 | 1382 | 905 | 1159 | 1455 |
| | South East | 676 | 864 | 1085 | 715 | 914 | 1149 | 755 | 965 | 1213 | 795 | 1016 | 1277 |
| | NW, SW East & Scotland | 614 | 786 | 987 | 650 | 832 | 1045 | 686 | 878 | 1103 | 723 | 925 | 1161 |
| | Mids, Yorks, NE & Wales | 588 | 751 | 944 | 622 | 795 | 1000 | 657 | 839 | 1055 | 691 | 884 | 1111 |

*These figures are indicative only and should ony be used as a guide and not as the basis for any expenditure or project. Please seek expert advice with regard to costs of land and buildings*

One of the best ways to keep costs down is to build simple

# How to Minimise Your Costs

Well, first of all, what is a minimal budget for a self-build project? Build cost tables indicate that the average build cost is around £1,200/m², but this average covers a wild variety of achieved costs.

## MINIMISE YOUR DESIGN FEES

Design fees can have a significant impact on your build budget – expect to pay £5-10,000 in fixed fees for design drawings from a qualified architect/ technician or between 8-12% of the build cost for the full supervisory service – which even on a low build cost of £150,000 is around £15,000 you simply can't afford to spend.

The good news is that you can minimise these costs significantly. If you follow the principles of simple design then you can come up with at the very least a concept drawing that you could hand to a local designer to work up into full planning and building drawings. You pay a big chunk of your design fees for the creativity and ideas of the designer – doing all of this beforehand means that you can reduce potentially £1,000s of costs to mere £100s. Alternatively, by using a design/build package company, you'll save having to pay upfront fees, although these tend to be clawed back in slightly higher-than-average materials costs. However, package companies do have expertise in bringing in projects to very low budgets, so they should definitely be an option to consider.

*If you follow the principles of simple design then you can come up with at the very least a concept drawing that you could hand to a local designer to work up*

CASE STUDY

BUDGET TIMBER FRAME

Kitchen units are from B&Q with plinths and back-lit glass unit doors from IKEA

## CONTEMPORARY AND STYLISH

**Gordon Aitken built his home in Fife for a remarkable £59,000 thanks to him taking on pretty much all of the building work – and the design. "We made savings employing only four tradesmen – the rest we did ourselves," he says. He also saved money by being smart with his purchases.**

'Accoya' timber cladding is real wood soaked in vinegar and then pressure-heated

## SIMPLIFY THE EXTERNAL DESIGN

You can set your project off on the right course at an early stage with a design that takes into account your lower budget expectations. The easiest house to build is, of course, a box shape (not just because it maximises laying runs, but also because it makes the roof shape as simple as possible, whether it's pitched or hipped). Just look at any developer-built housing estate – it's usually crammed with houses based on the above principles, which just happen to be similar to those employed in Georgian house design.

You can minimise build costs even further at this stage by designing out many of the potentially expensive features. No-one's suggesting you build a house without windows, but do you need quite so many, what size are they, and what design? Clearly, the less and smaller the windows, the better. The same goes for chimneys and potentially design-blighting but money saving options like porches.

## GET INVOLVED AT SOME LEVEL

A chequebook self-build – one where your personal involvement is limited to paying people – is likely to be an expensive self-build. The more you can do, in any capacity, the more money you will save – from at the very simplest level labouring on site (which will save you a labourer's day rate, about £100) through to project management fees (a project manager will typically add on 10% to all material and labour costs).

Be sure that you're adding value. A plumber won't be terribly grateful for your attempts to help out if it's slowing him down (meaning higher fees). Likewise, if you're not able to actually manage a building project, and have no idea of construction schedules, then your 10% saving will be quickly eaten up by wasted days on site. If you want to go down the project management route as a first-time self-builder, make sure you invest in some good books (available at ovolobooks.co.uk) and pick up David Snell's Project Planner wallchart (available from David at H&R shows). Just as importantly, you'll need the local knowledge to be able to find good tradesmen, which is difficult if you're new to the area.

*Be sure that you're adding value. A plumber won't be terribly grateful for your attempts to help out if it's slowing him down (meaning higher fees)*

Perhaps the most sensible option is to discuss with your builder where savings can be made. Builders in general are certainly keener to get work than they were two years ago and as such would be more amenable to helping you shave costs in return for still getting the job. One tactic that works particularly well is to employ a builder on a split basis, meaning that you'll employ him to get you to weathertight stage – and then you can take over to run the interior side of things.

On a smaller scale perhaps better suited to those with little time but a lot of enthusiasm, it's possible to split down a contract with a builder to leave out certain tasks. Those that make most sense for a keen money

SAVING MONEY

### A BASIC SPECIFICATION

**The materials and features you choose for your house come in a huge variety of prices. Expensive bricks are six times the price of cheaper ones, and so you'll need to research the prices and qualities of a range of products and structural options. The decisions you make will have a direct impact on how much money you spend – so for instance, choosing a suspended timber floor over a concrete slab will save you money. A small new house will need (at approx 60 bricks/m² facing) around 9,000 bricks. At £175/1,000 compared to £1,000/1,000 for handmades, that decision alone will save you £7,425. Opting for a basic heating set-up (basic pressed steel radiators and combi boiler rather than underfloor heating, system boiler, pressurised hot water cylinder, woodburner and controls) will probably save you in the region of £3-5,000. Choosing softwood or PVCu windows over hardwood will also make a significant saving.**

saving self-builder to get involved in are decorating and landscaping – in truth because less things can go wrong. Decorating above all is a non-time sensitive task that, while surprisingly intense (imagine painting all the walls and ceilings in your house three times) can be accomplished on weekends and evenings at the end of the project and might save you between £5-10,000. You'll need to be able to fit skirting boards, flooring, tiling and so on, but these aren't tasks beyond the wit of a typical self-builder (or a typical self-builder's wise father-in-law). Landscaping is certainly more physically demanding (it helps if you do it as you go along) but, again, is not a critical-path task.

*A sensible option is to discuss with your builder where savings can be made. Builders in general are certainly keener to get work than they were two years ago*

## SHOP SMART

Small discounts and shop-smart savvy can go a long way on a self-build project – the biggest shopping trip of your life. On a £150,000 project materials are likely to account for between £50-100,000 worth of expenditure, so it pays to make sure you're getting good deals. Getting all of those items at a 5% discount means saving between £2,500-£5,000 on your project.

The key first of all is to establish an account with a local builder's merchant – they will be a critical source of regular building materials that you will undoubtedly need along the way. Make them aware of the work you'll be putting their way and try and negotiate a fixed discount. Secondly, use the internet – it's definitely the quickest way to find cheap deals on all sorts of goods. A quick look for a Duravit Happy D basin (750mm) brought up prices ranging from £152-189 (a 20% saving). Imagine the money you could save using the internet to source discounted internal fittings (particularly flooring, tiles, kitchens and bathrooms). It's less effective for building materials although this sector is starting to develop its online presence too (buildingsuppliesrus.co.uk).

CASE STUDY

OPEN-PLAN CONTEMPORARY

Costs were kept down by keeping the design compact

### ISLAND HOME ON DELIVERED ON A BUDGET

**Chris Mortimer and Lucrecia Luque's contemporary-style, open plan home has all the design elements and quality of a high-end, high-budget project – but the home, on Skye, cost them just £66,000 to build.**

This four bedroom family home in Lancashire was built for under £80,000 thanks to plenty of DIY help from family and friends

Organisation is key to cost-effective self-build. Crane hire expensive so needs to be planned so that it is required for as short a time as possible

# PART FIVE

# HOW TO RUN YOUR *self-build* PROJECT

Self-building encompasses a variety of different routes to getting your own home built. But how do you decide which one is best for you?.

It's one of the great anomalies of the self-build world that, for the overwhelming majority of individuals building their own home, the actual level of physical involvement on site – literally building it yourself – is next to non-existent. 'Self-building' in fact encompasses a whole range of different approaches but as long as you're finding your own building plot, deciding on an individual house design to suit your own unique needs and choosing the products to go into that home, you can proudly wear a badge that says 'self-builder' on it. Choosing how to get to that goal, however, involves carefully evaluating your own circumstances and deciding what you can bring to the party. This section is designed to help you understand what the key routes involve and which one might best suit you.

**DEFINITIONS**

*It helps to clarify exactly what it is we're talking about when we talk about individual roles in the building world.*

**MAIN CONTRACTOR:**
**The person who employs individual tradesmen (such as brickies and electricians) when necessary on a building project. They are likely to have a wide range of local contacts and be able to call on tradesmen at short notice periods. They are also likely to get involved with work on site and fill in the gaps.**

**PROJECT MANAGER:**
**Simply one of the functions of a main contractor. Project managers do not necessarily get involved physically on site but are likely to be constantly on the phone organising trades and materials deliveries. They are responsible for bringing in the building project on schedule.**

**SUBCONTRACTORS:**
**A subcontractor is a tradesman who works for a main contractor. They are the electricians, brickies, carpenters and plumbers who are not paid directly by the self-builder. If a self-builder is project managing the site, these tradesmen actually become simply contractors, as they are directly employed.**

# *Using a Main Contractor*

## HOW IT WORKS:

The self-builder employs a main contractor to run the building site on a day-to-day basis. This will usually involve the main contractor being responsible for organising a smooth flow of labour onto the site when necessary (and paying them directly), dealing with the unloading of deliveries, organising warranty and building regulations inspections, running the site itself (e.g. toilet facilities, storage of materials and so on) and working from the design plans. In addition, depending on your arrangement, the main contractor might also be responsible for ordering materials and ensuring they are on site when necessary.

## YOUR INPUT:

You will of course be responsible for hiring the main contractor in the first instance – so choose well. In addition, you'll need to ensure that the main contractor has detailed building drawings to work from and, crucially, a detailed specification of materials (whether he is ordering them himself or not) – as early in the process as possible. You should be prepared to visit the site at least once a week to check on progress, ensure that the drawings are being followed, and that the main contractor has everything he needs. It's also important psychologically for the main contractor to see that his work is being appreciated and encouraged. You will still need to be able to maintain telephone contact at any time for emergencies or questions as they arise – communication is critical.

*It's also important psychologically for the main contractor to see that his work is being appreciated and encouraged.*

## COST AND CASHFLOW IMPLICATIONS:

Although the main contractor will be responsible for paying the subcontractors, you will need to ensure a regular payment to the main contractor. Many main contractors will give a fixed price quote at the tendering stage and will present you with a monthly invoice (showing the balance still owing along with any 'extras') that you should be prepared to pay promptly. If you are leaving materials purchasing up to your main contractor, be aware that while many have trade accounts (and

CASE STUDY

STEEL-FRAME CONTEMPORARY-STYLE

Glyn and Jane Martin used a glazier, electrician, plumber, roofers, frame erectors and excavators but did much of the rest themselves

## MUCH OF THE WORK WAS COMPLETED BY THE OWNERS

Jane and Glyn Martin stayed on site to be involved in the process of building their contemporary-style home. Building was largely on a DIY basis with contractors used to excavate the site, erect the steel frame and clad the roof with zinc. "Building the house has certainly brought us closer," says Jane, "and it's rewarding to think how much we completed ourselves".

1. The steel frame structure is erected on the foundations.
2. The roof structure takes shape, with timber beams providing support.
3. Glyn and Jane spent the best part of two years on site, handling much of the labour themselves.
4. The new house begins to overshadow the existing bungalow.
5. The existing bungalow is then knocked down and the space is used for the extensive patio.
6. Glyn laid the stone wall himself, following it round to the garage.

Working with a builder will reduce the potential savings you make by self-building, but is essential if you are unable to devote much time to being on site

therefore long credit terms) with many key suppliers, you might be required to pay upfront for some items. If this is the case, ensure that you get them ordered in your name.

A main contractor will rely on a percentage uplift or 'add-on' to the quotes he gets from his subcontractors in order to pay him for his own time. This varies according to the market, but is likely to be around 20-40% on top of labour and materials prices. It's highly likely that if you go down this route you'll never know – and probably never want to know! However, many self-builders who go down this route view the main contractor's margin as money well spent to avoid the stresses and strains of running a building site day-to-day.

**PROS**

- **Reduces daily stresses of running a site;**
- **There's always someone on site to ask if things go wrong and someone to fall back on;**
- **The main contractor has an instant supply of local labour that you'll never be able to replicate, particularly if you're moving to a new area;**
- **Will fill in the grey areas between trades that you would otherwise have to;**
- **Reduces the amount of communication you'll need to have with tradesmen in areas you might not know much about.**

**CONS**

- **Between 20-40% more expensive than managing your own site;**
- **Reduces the feeling of personal involvement with a project;**
- **Doesn't absolve you of the responsibility for checking work;**
- **The quotation/tendering process is arduous and may not be particularly competitive.**

## IDEALLY SUITED TO:

Busy full-time workers and those who live a long way from their building site; people who have never built their own home before and might not be confident of the process. While you'll still need to be able to get to site at short notice and field telephone calls, it takes the daily stresses away.

# Being your Own Project Manager

## HOW IT WORKS:

The self-builder would be responsible for the day to day running of the building project. This would involve: interpreting the building drawings on site; finding, scheduling and directly paying tradesmen from groundworkers to plumbers; organising and running the site, from hiring toilet facilities and security fencing to keeping the site tidy and dealing with the grey areas between trades; taking deliveries and working out where to store materials safely; ordering and paying upfront for materials and ensuring they get delivered when needed; and liaising with warranty and building inspectors. Effectively, the smooth running of project is entirely down to the self-builder.

*You'll need to be able to visit the site before work starts (8am is the traditional start of a tradesman's day) and once work has finished – every day until the end of the project.*

## YOUR INPUT:

As above. You'll need to be able to visit the site before work starts (8am is the traditional start of a tradesman's day) and once work has finished – every day until the end of the project. In addition, you'll need to be able to get to the site at a moment's notice to deal with deliveries, meet building inspectors, service providers and so on. There is also likely to be some DIY involvement as you'll need to fill in between the trades.

*Many lenders offer release of stage payments in arrears of work being done, you'll need to arrange temporary bridging finance to pay tradesmen at the end of every week.*

## COST AND CASHFLOW IMPLICATIONS:

Project management requires early contact with trades and materials suppliers in order to be able to come up with a realistic budget — critical if you need to arrange finance and important to manage properly to keep a tight reign on cashflow during the build. As many lenders offer release of stage payments in arrears of work being done, you'll probably need to arrange temporary bridging finance to pay tradesmen at the end of every week. Alternatively, you could investigate specialist advanced funding through Buildstore (www.buildstore.co.uk) or Advanced Flexible Self-build Mortgage (www.afsbm.co.uk), which will provide money up front. You'll obviously be able to save the builder's profit (as mentioned above, anywhere between 20-40% on labour and materials) but bear in mind that experienced local builders are more likely to be able to negotiate better discounts/trade prices on materials and, to an extent, on labour. Ensure that you establish a relationship with a local merchant and set up credit terms to help with cashflow.

**PROS**

- **Saves the main contractor's markup – anywhere between 20-40% on labour and materials;**
- **Not working with a fixed price contract enables certain flexibility with specification and design during the project;**
- **You'll feel a lot closer to the project and really know every detail of the construction.**

**CONS**

- **Requires considerable time and input from the self-builder – visiting site twice a day and constantly fielding calls and dealing with problems;**
- **Much more stressful;**
- **You'll need to be incredibly organised;**
- **You'll need a good network of local contacts;**
- **You'll have to be able to work closely with trades and check their work;**
- **There's no-one to discuss issues with or fall back on should things go wrong.**

## IDEALLY SUITED TO:

People with plenty of time on their hands – or a lot of flexibility in their full-time jobs - who can handle stress and uncertainty; living close to site and able to understand the building process.

# Package Company

## HOW IT WORKS:

Package companies – also called 'turnkey' suppliers or 'design and build' companies – provide, as the name suggests, a one-stop-shop solution to the housebuilding process. They usually offer design, labour/construction and material supply as part of a fixed price contract. While the majority of package companies operate in the timber frame sector - where they offer manufacture of the frame and erection – a small number of package suppliers offer traditional masonry construction. The good news is that the traditional view of these companies - that they offer a limited range of standard house designs and tie the self-builder into a complete and expensive one-stop solution with a modest choice of finishing materials – is no longer applicable. The majority now offer an effective, bespoke approach that can be individually tailored to a self-builder's requirements and circumstances – for instance, offering bespoke designs from an in-house designer; having a list of approved contractors to choose from rather than a staff team; and the ability in some instances to opt out of parts of the package and choose your own finishing materials. The reality of this competitive market is that the self-builder can find a package company that will assist their project in any way they require.

*The reality of this competitive market is that the self-builder can find a package company that will assist their project in any way they require.*

The usual route, for illustrative purposes, is for the package supplier to carry out an initial site assessment; come up with a design and deal with planning issues; either manufacture the frame or arrange for materials to be delivered (or both); arrange labour or assist in finding it (and liaise directly with the labour); provide finishing materials. Some may be willing to carry out project management services.

## YOUR INPUT:

Limited – which is the key reason why people choose this route. In theory the self-builder can get as involved as they would like to both on a project management or physical basis.

## COST AND CASHFLOW IMPLICATIONS:

Most package companies in the timber frame sector require payment upfront as a commitment before the manufacture and supply of the frame (indeed this was one of the initial reasons behind the conception of the advanced funding mortgages described above). In general terms, all package companies, while offering free design services, will require regular payments (as a percentage of the total fixed price contract) throughout the process – perhaps 1% upon agreeing to proceed, 2% for detailed drawings, 25% during early construction work, and so on. It depends very much on the individual circumstances of the company and what service you are expecting – but be prepared to pay initial sums early in the process.

The package company route is likely to cost more than either supplying materials yourself and is comparable to getting your builder to supply materials for you. You will save, however, the significant early payments that an architect would require and, in addition, will benefit from the knowledge that the package company's designers are well versed in relating their designs to your build budget – something independent architects are not necessarily renowned for. This alone makes the extra costs worthwhile for many self-builders.

*The package company route is likely to cost more than either supplying materials yourself and is comparable to getting your builder to supply materials for you.*

**PROS**

- **Saves dealing with architects and ensures build costs are realistically tied in with the house design;**
- **The most hassle-free way to build;**
- **Many package companies have lists of**

CASE STUDY

GERMAN PACKAGE-BUILD

## PURCHASED FROM A SHOWROOM

**Allan and Lindsey Taylor used German package company Huf Haus to design, build and erect their contemporary style home. Allan and Lindsey visited the German company's showroom, making key choices and finalising the design details, before the house was built in Germany and driven to the UK. From start to finish it took three months to complete.**

Allan and Lindsey's home was designed, built and erected by German package supplier Huf Haus

**approved contractors, bypassing the difficult issues of finding labour;**
- **Package companies provide reassurance and moral support during the process;**
- **Their buying power enables them to negotiate discounts with key materials suppliers that individuals might not be able to enjoy;**
- **Some package companies provide assistance with initial issues like finding and assessing land, planning permission and building regulations that would otherwise be left to the self-builder.**

**CONS**
- **Limiting your own input invariably means paying for someone else's – this is not a cheap alternative, although it might be cost-effective;**
- **The quality of the design depends on the skills of a limited choice of in-house designers – some are great, some are moderate;**
- **Some package companies offer a limited choice of finishing materials;**
- **Many require significant upfront payments.**

## IDEALLY SUITED TO:

Self-builders who require a helping hand with their project, because they are busy or inexperienced with the building industry. Package companies provide solutions to the numerous problems that self-builders face: from finding and assessing land to finding labour. Self-builders are also often attracted to package companies by the quality of the range of house designs on offer.

## WORKING WITH BUILDERS

*Builders have a terrible reputation in the media but 99% of self-builders will agree with that maxim "What you put in, you get out." Treat your builder well and you are much more likely not only to get on, but to get a better quality of commitment from him. Here is how to treat them nice (and get the best out of them):*

### PAY ON TIME:

**Agree how and when payments will be made and how they will be structured. Don't hold back money unnecessarily – most builders have large overdrafts and this puts them in a vulnerable position financially. They are relying on you for regular income and you'll need to provide it. Otherwise, they will be out of pocket and will begin to look elsewhere. If you're having cashflow problems you'll have to be open with the builder. In most cases they will understand.**

### COMMUNICATE:

**Regularly ask how things are going, when certain targets are likely to be met and, of course, discuss changes openly (and the implications for prices). That way, any issues are headed off before they become a major problem.**

### BE NICE:

**Builders take pride in their work and you should view your builder as a partner rather than simply an employee. Where possible, ask for their advice and avoid confrontational approaches: a calm "When do you think this might be done?" is so much better than a high-pitched "Why hasn't this been done yet?" You might not ever be best friends, but for the duration of the project, you'll need to encourage rather than always be on the lookout for problems.**

### BE FLEXIBLE:

**Things are not always going to go to plan on a building project; the design might have to change; subcontractors might not turn up (or even the builders, for a few days at a time); work might need re-doing or materials might be unavailable for months rather than the short time you'd hoped. A flexible approach is critical. Don't be a stickler for detail and always appreciate the big picture. Builders tend to take on other jobs at the same time as yours to enable a smooth workflow so be laid back (at least initially) rather than dictatorial. Treat them as you would expect to be treated yourself and, above all, don't forget that the building world is a very different one to the industry you work in. Try and fit in and accept that, if you can be reasonable, you're likely to get better results.**

CASE STUDY

GREAT VALUE SELF-BUILD

Gary and Hayley Thomas handled much of the on-site work during their project, saving £1,000s

## HOUSE BUILT IN SPARE TIME OVER 18 MONTHS

**Gary Thomas built the majority of his and wife Hayley's mid-Wales three-bed home. He had some experience in building which definitely helped with the confidence factor, but because he did it in his spare time the project took 18 months. "It just takes some imagination, belief in the potential and quite a bit of time and effort making the idea a reality," he says.**

The house cost just £85,000 to build.

# DIY

## HOW IT WORKS:

You'll be responsible for physically building the house from scratch yourself. While there are certain tasks that you won't be able to carry out without the help of qualified professionals (unless you intend to take training), it is in theory possible to construct a whole house using your own labour. In addition, of course, you'll be responsible for interpreting design drawings, ordering materials (and therefore having a good grasp of quantities), liaising with warranty and building inspectors, taking deliveries and organising the day-to-day running of the site.

*You'll need to combine the physically demanding tasks of groundwork, bricklaying and roofing with skilled tasks such as plumbing and plastering.*

## YOUR INPUT:

See above. You'll need to combine the physically demanding tasks of groundwork, bricklaying and roofing with skilled tasks such as plumbing and plastering. There is, of course, nothing to stop you mixing your own labour with bought-in labour where required; bear in mind that your own lack of experience might mean that you are likely to be slower than those around you and you'll need to ensure that you're not holding up the build process.

## COSTS AND CASHFLOW IMPLICATIONS:

DIY is the only way it's possible these days to build individual houses for incredibly tiny sums of money – using all your own labour and buying your own (contract quality) materials it's possible to build a new home for less than £50,000. Cashflow implications are much easier to manage than with the other routes as the only outgoings are for materials, for which you should arrange credit terms. You'll need to factor into the equation, however – particularly if you're giving up work for a couple of years to take on this role – the lost earnings you'll miss out on in addition to the extra interest payments and other costs incurred through your undoubtedly slower progress.

**PROS**

- **massive cost savings;**
- **complete control over the project and no worries about finding labour;**
- **huge sense of achievement and a complete knowledge of every detail of your finished house.**

**HEADING**

### TIPS FOR SUCCESSFUL PROJECT MANAGEMENT

- **find and contact local tradesmen during the planning process and get them organised ready to start when you need them;**
- **run a site office with copies of plans, standard site equipment, a phone and shelter;**
- **keep a diary of each day's events and organise your quotations, certificates, plans, receipts and contacts meticulously;**
- **draw up a project schedule which will help you organise when labour and materials are required;**
- **organise materials deliveries so that you don't have expensive materials lying around in unlocked places;**
- **keep the site tidy each day – it will speed up work the day after and minimise accidents;**
- **find time to plan: don't get caught up in the detail of each day's progress – you'll need to be constantly thinking ahead;**
- **make decisions early and stick to them – the hubbub of a busy building site is no time to be making snap decisions about kitchens, flooring and design issues. Plan ahead and use the slow months before work commences to research materials and ideas thoroughly;**
- **Account for the VAT reclaim in your upfront cashflow plans. In other words, you will get much of the VAT you spend back in the months after the build has finished, but you'll still need to find the cash to pay for it upfront.**

**CONS**

- **factor in the lost earnings you're sacrificing;**
- **progress will be a lot slower than with professionals;**
- **the quality of work produced might not be professional standard;**
- **warranty and building inspectors are likely to be a lot more stringent in their checks;**
- **lenders might be more reluctant to finance a DIY project as it is deemed to be more of a risk.**

## IDEALLY SUITED TO:

Either people who have been around the building industry and are willing to give up their time or retirees who have a practical mind and can view the project as a hobby.

## CONCLUSION

Truly successful self-builds come in all shapes and sizes and each project is as individual as the circumstances of each self-builder. The key is understanding what you can add to the project and, just as importantly, what your limiting factors are: whether it be time, lack of building skills or inexperience. The biggest self-build failures occur when people underestimate how difficult and time consuming the building process can be and get themselves in too deep. Likewise, those looking for massive cost savings need to understand that the more work and effort they put in – in addition to labour – they more they will save. Don't make false economies. The fact remains that, while hiring a main contractor is no guarantee of a smooth project, the majority of self-builds that overrun and suffer the problem of building sites with no-one working on them are self-managed. Ultimately, however, no amount of money paid to main contractors and other professionals - even package suppliers - is an excuse to not manage a self-build project. It's when self-builders don't put enough of themselves into a project that things can go horribly wrong.

Design and build package companies offer what's called a 'Turnkey' option – literally meaning all you have to do is turn the key to get into your new home

**MIX AND MATCH**

### CHOOSE THE ARRANGEMENT THAT WORKS BEST FOR YOU

**The reality of the self-build situation – and one engendered to a large part by the growing importance of the self-build industry and its competitive nature – is that many self-builders decide to mix and match several of the above approaches. Projects can be split into different sections – commonly up to, and after, weathertight stage is reached – and different approaches taken for each section. For instance, some package companies might be willing to let you take their design services and materials supply up to weathertight stage only; you might feel that you can handle the decorating and landscaping yourself but need a builder to manage the rest of the project for you; you might want a project manager for the critical first half of the build but feel you can handle organising the internal trades yourself. It really is up to you to work out an arrangement that works best.**

# RAISING THE *finance* FOR A SELF-BUILD HOME

# *Self-build Mortgages*

## HOW MUCH CAN I BORROW?

The amount you can borrow for a self-build mortgage will depend on the same factors that decide how much you can borrow for a regular house mortgage. In most cases this will either be based on income multipliers (3-4x single income, 1.5 x joint) or, more often, affordability factors (lenders will assess your regular monthly outgoings and income set against how much the monthly loan will cost to repay).

This figure will then be assessed against loan to value (LTV) policies. These policies change weekly but, for example, lenders will provide funding for up to 80% of the value of the plot and 80% of the value of the building project.

*The mortgage specifically designed for the needs of a self-build project. Money is drawn down in a series of stages rather than as a whole.*

## WHAT IS A SELF-BUILD MORTGAGE?

A self-build mortgage is a specialist type of mortgage specifically designed for the needs of a self-build project. Money is drawn down in a series of stages rather than as a whole. Usually, the first stage is on completion of the purchase of the building plot. Subsequent stages – usually six – are released as the project progresses, e.g. foundations, wallplate, weathertight, first fix, etc.

## WHERE DO I GO TO GET SELF-BUILD FINANCE?

It's always worth checking with your existing lender or high street bank to see what arrangements can be made. It's possible – although not probable – that they might be able to offer funding through an overdraft facility or commercial-style development loan.

For specialist self-build mortgages, you will need to go through one of the two specialist brokers (Buildstore or Self-builder) or if you want funds released in advance of the stages being completed, regular arrears stage releases can also be found.

For a full list of companies offering self-build mortgages, along with details on loan to values and

contact details, please visit www.selfbuild.co.uk

## HOW WOULD AN EXAMPLE PROJECT BE FINANCED?

This is based on a plot purchase of £200,000 and a build cost of £150,000.

The self-builder gets a self-build mortgage based on an LTV of 80%. He pays a £40,000 deposit from partial proceeds of the sale of his previous home, and services the £160,000 mortgage payments until such time as work proceeds. He then draws down the remaining £120,000 of the mortgage as work progresses, filling in the gaps in funding using his own capital.

By the end of the project, he has a mortgage of £280,000, having spent a total of £350,000 on the self-built home. In most instances the mortgage is then ported to a regular house mortgage.

# How to Reclaim VAT on a Self-build or Conversion Project

As you don't have to pay VAT if you're building a new house from a developer, HMRC have made allowances for self-builders and converters to enjoy the same VAT free benefits.

*Renovators do not enjoy any of the VAT benefits that self-builders and converters enjoy and will have to pay VAT in full.*

**THE RULES**

## NEW BUILD

Self-builders can reclaim any – or almost all – of the VAT they pay during the course of their project on materials and services. VAT-registered builders and tradesmen should zero-rate their invoices, while, of course, if they're not VAT-registered, they shouldn't be charging it you anyway.

If a main contractor is buying materials on your behalf, they should not pass on any VAT liability to you (they can claim it back under their own returns). If they do, ensure you get the original receipt. If you're buying materials for yourself, you will have to pay VAT at source, but you will need to keep the receipt and submit a reclaim form at the end of the project (see later).

## CONVERSIONS

Converters can once again reclaim the full amount of VAT paid on any materials purchases for their project, but VAT-registered builders and tradesmen will charge you VAT at the reduced rate of 5%, which cannot be reclaimed.

## RENOVATIONS

Renovators do not enjoy any of the VAT benefits that self-builders and converters enjoy and will have to pay VAT in full. As a result many renovators like to use non-VAT registered builders to at least reduce the liability for labour costs.

However, there are some concessions in place for renovators who take on the renovation of buildings that have been empty for some time. If the house has been empty for at least 10 years, it is treated as a conversion (see above). If the house has been empty for between two and ten years, there is a concession that allows VAT-registered builders to charge 5% VAT on a supply and fix contract (i.e. they buy the materials for you).

## WHAT CAN YOU RECLAIM?

In general, you can reclaim for all materials that are fixed into the house, although the interpretation of this can be quite complex. For instance, you can reclaim VAT on wooden flooring, but not carpet, and fitted wardrobes but not freestanding. You cannot reclaim VAT for design fees or services.

## HOW TO RECLAIM VAT

You can only reclaim VAT directly from HMRC by filling out either form VAT431NB (for New Builds) or VAT431C (for Conversions). You can download them from http://customs.hmrc.gov.uk. These notices replace VAT Notice 719 by combining the guidance notes with the claim form.

You can only reclaim VAT once and it has to be after the issue of a completion certificate or proof of habitation. You must fill out the claim form, attach all of your relevant invoices/receipts, and return it to the claims office in Birmingham, with your bank details.

You will receive acknowledgement of your claim within two weeks, when any queries will be raised. HMRC aims to repay any successful claim into your account within eight weeks, although this figure varies wildly.

CASE STUDY

Sheila also enjoyed being involved, and we're both pretty well organised so there were no rows or disagreements...

**"I'M A CHARTERED** surveyor by profession, and co-director of a building company, but this is the first time that I've built my own house," explains Richard Hope, who with wife Sheila has built a fabulous oak frame home (from TJ Crump Oakwrights) in Sussex. "I was keen to act as project manager and to take on some of the work myself, including keeping the site clean and tidy. Sheila also enjoyed getting involved, and we're both pretty well organised so there were no rows or disagreements during the build — despite the fact we were putting in long hours before and after work."

The Hopes thoroughly enjoyed their project and struggle to recall any low points during the nine-month build.

"Everything about this house is robust and low-maintenance, says Richard." Visitors always comment on how relaxing it feels," he adds

Many of the tradespeople who worked on the house were friends

SECTION THREE

# GETTING *practical*

# STRUCTURAL *choices*

## BUILDING SYSTEMS

### AN INTRODUCTION

There are many different options that you face when you build a new house. If you aren't terribly bothered about how your house looks 'under the bonnet' then you can quite easily opt out of making a choice at all and go with your builder's default settings. Let's get one thing clear – in the vast majority of cases the way in which your house is built, i.e. the structural component, will have no impact at all on how it looks. You need to separate out the outside shell of the house (the cladding) from the inside structural walls, which actually hold the house and roof up. Your choice of internal structure doesn't impact (in most cases) on the outside facing of the house – so you can have a house that has stone, brick, timber or render on the outside and timber, blockwork or one of the other options on the inside. You won't be able to spot from the outside whether a house is timber framed or built of concrete blocks.

The more you look into the concept of self-building, however, the more you are likely to want to make a choice in between the various systems available. The default setting in England and Wales is an internal blockwork structure with a facing of brick. There is a gap between the two walls, which is known as a cavity (hence the term cavity wall construction). The gap is usually filled with insulation. In Scotland, and in growing numbers across the rest of the UK, more and more self-builders and commercial builders are using a form of timber frame construction – combined with an outside shell of usually brick, render or timber cladding.

So if the impact of this choice is not visual, then what is it? Well, the way your house is built will have an influence (only an influence) on the way it performs, and the experience on site. One building system might be quicker on site than another; one might make it easier to meet certain energy efficiency requirements. Another might be more expensive and have better sound insulation properties.

Here is a quick overview of the key systems:

Timber frame systems come in different shapes and sizes – from more traditional open panel systems…

…to closed panel systems, where the walls are pre-formed

# CHOOSING TIMBER FRAME

Timber frame is once again gaining in popularity in both the speculative and self-build sectors of the UK housing market. Some 42,000 houses were built using timber frame construction across the housing market in 2004 and the anecdotal evidence from any large-scale building site is that what once was a fairly niche part of the homebuilding world is now very much part of the mainstream. Although across the UK the proportion of new homes built using this method is 17%, this figure actually hides a wild variation in the pattern in different areas. Whilst in England around 11% of new homes are built using timber frame construction, in Scotland this figure jumps to a huge 65%. The growth rate across the UK is some 18% – double that of more 'conventional' building systems.

It's tempting, therefore, to say that while timber frame is undoubtedly growing in popularity, there is also much more room for growth: by international standards, the UK falls well short when it comes to the proportion of new homes built using timber frame. It's also tempting to conclude that timber frame is very much the construction method of the future, flexible, plentiful and sustainable.

Timber frame, albeit in a very different form, is also one of the great housing construction systems of the past. Many of the green oak manufacturers so popular today (mentioned later) recreate what is conventionally regarded as the first form of timber framing, which originated in the 17th century. This used locally sourced hardwoods, such as oak, cut into a structural frame of posts and beams, infilled with locally available materials, typically timber lathe known as 'wattle' covered in a mixture of mud, horsehair and animal dung known as 'daub' and then finished in lime render

> 'Timber frame' is a term used to describe a raft of different timber-based construction systems and is surrounded by claim and counterclaim.

## WHY BUILDERS LIKE TIMBER

- **Convenience of a single supplier providing design and a weather tight shell erected on site;**
- **The option to have a 140mm insulated frame;**
- **Easier to make the shell airtight;**
- **Quicker to build once on site and ability to work on internal trades at an earlier stage;**
- **Timber is a sustainable form of construction.**

and plaster. It was a form of construction that rapidly lost appeal following the Great Fire of London in 1666, however, timber was resurrected as a structural building material in 19th century USA, where modern-day framing techniques – where the frame is pre-fabricated and then erected on site – were born. In the USA, timber frame has never looked back — and it has enjoyed meteoric growth across Europe in the 20th century, with the UK (or more specifically England) being one of the last nations to really catch on.

Timber frames are generally considered to be quicker to build on site: the superstructure of the house can be assembled and made weather tight in a matter of days which means that the internal trades can begin whilst the exterior is being clad. Coupled with the fact that so many of the timber frame suppliers offer a 'package' service including design, manufacture and erection of the frame, it's not difficult to see why this form of housebuilding is so popular amongst self-builders.

As with many aspects of the building industry, timber frame construction has developed a mythology which the astute self-builder will need to fight through.

## THE BUILD SPEED MYTH:

### TIMBER FRAMES ARE FASTER

There is little doubt that, once on site, a timber frame is quicker to erect than a conventional masonry blockwork shell. It can indeed take as little as a week for the main frame to be erected and weather tight. Unfortunately for self-builders, this is only one of several considerations they need to take into account when assessing build speed. Many of the key timber frame suppliers have lead-in times of up to three months for the delivery of the frame to site: time that could of course be spent building using blocks. In addition, the actual proportion of the whole project spent on constructing the external shell is typically only around 30-40%, meaning that while timber frames are quicker once on site, self-builders may be surprised by how little difference this makes to the whole schedule unless they sequence the finishing trades very efficiently.

## THE PRICE MYTH:

### TIMBER FRAMES COST MORE

The actual service/product provided varies considerably from one timber frame supplier to another and in most part, the difference in cost comes down to the specification and what is included or excluded in the package. A basic 90mm timber frame can cost as little as £60-70/m$^2$ of floor area for an open panel softwood frame, excluding erection, doors, windows and internal joinery.

On a like-for-like cost basis with masonry, timber frame is very similar. Any difference in price will be due to the cost and availability of timber and labour – carpenters vs. blocklayers. In Scotland timber frame tends to be slightly cheaper than masonry, whilst the opposite is true in the rest of the UK. The type of external cladding used is also a cost factor. Timber frame is invariably cheaper than masonry when clad in render – a very popular choice in Scotland. It is also worth bearing in mind that the structural walls of a house only account for around 8-10% of total build costs, so the overall impact of any cost differential between timber frame and masonry will be negligible.

## THE ENERGY EFFICIENCY MYTH:

### TIMBER FRAME HOMES ARE WARMER

For many years the standard 90mm timber frame wall had a superior level of insulation to the standard masonry cavity wall which, until the Building Regulations were tightened, often contained no insulation at all other than an aerated concrete block. This gave rise to the idea that timber frame homes are more energy efficient – which they on average would have been. Today, however, a house using any form of

## WHAT DO YOU GET FOR YOUR MONEY...

**The service provided can vary dramatically from one timber frame company to another. Some companies will simply provide the superstructure; others will provide a full design and build service. Most companies offer a package which includes design of the house, manufacture of the frame and the option of erection on site, usually by an independent gang of subcontractors. Many of the self-proclaimed 'package' suppliers will actually be willing to offer simpler services, too.**

*Many of the timber frame package suppliers will be willing to offer simpler services as well*

**A simple package includes:**

- **Sole plates, damp-proof courses and clips;**
- **Structural external/internal wall panels and waterproof house wraps;**
- **Floor joists and floor covers (not finishes) – in Scotland, this tends to include a timber ground floor as well but elsewhere timber ground floors are rare;**
- **All roof elements, usually supplied as prefabricated trusses;**
- **Option of external joinery (often supplied unglazed).**

**Items that may or may not be included:**

- **Wall ties, lintels and cavity barriers;**
- **Insulation and vapour barriers;**
- **Internal second fix joinery, stairs, doors, skirtings, architraves, etc.**
- **Plasterboard.**

**Items that are unlikely to be included unless the whole housebuilding contract is left to the timber frame company:**

- **Groundworks and substructure materials or labour;**
- **Drainage materials and services;**
- **External claddings and damp-proof courses for these;**
- **Roofing materials: felt, batten, roof tiles, etc;**
- **Floor screeds;**
- **Chimney flues or structure**
- **Mastic sealers and glazing (through joinery is increasingly being supplied pre-glazed);**
- **Heating, plumbing and electrics;**
- **Plaster finishes (skim coats, dry-lining, Artex, coving);**
- **Kitchen units, fitted bedroom furniture and sanitaryware;**
- **Decorating, wall and floor tiling and finishes;**
- **Garage doors;**
- **Externals: paving, fencing and landscaping.**

**You should look carefully at the specification offered by each company and check that you are comparing like with like. Many brochures offer indicative prices for the elements that are not supplied with the kit, so use these to extrapolate final build costs. Again, this can be misleading because the assumed costs are never the same, nor even the way area is measured.**

Log homes walls are constructed of logs of varying thicknesses incorporating double tongue-and-groove with draft-proof interlocking

This Huf Haus uses a pre-fabricated post and beam structure.

Oak timber frame like this Oakwrights example is both structural and decorative

Wall panel of this kind of German design are built in a factory and delivered in completed sections

construction can be upgraded to provide a high level of energy efficiency by adding more insulation into the layers of the wall structure.

The large clear voids between the studs in a 90mm timber frame wall panel lend themselves to being filled with insulation – usually mineral wool – however, this can no longer meet the elemental U-value required by the latest building regulations without additional, or superior insulation being added into the mix. The wall thickness can either be widened to 140-150mm to take more insulation, or, more cost-effectively, a high-performance mineral wool can be used. It is also possible to use insulated plasterboard or an insulated vapour check inside.

## THE ATTITUDE MYTH:

### THE PUBLIC DOESN'T TRUST TIMBER FRAME

The housing industry is even slower at taking on new ideas than the public, which hasn't helped timber frame to become immediately popular. The self-builder concerned that they might be building an unsaleable timber frame house should worry not: a significant number of large developers (such as Westbury) are using timber frames (often the open panel system, more on which later) which should be in itself a confirmation of the commercial viability of the system. In terms of selling price, it's only really at the structural

survey stage that it will even become an issue because the average estate agent or buyer wouldn't be able to tell the construction system just by looking at the house from the outside (the traditional tapping of walls means very little these days thanks to the prevalence of dry-lining). Any surveyor will view timber frame as a conventional system and advise accordingly.

## THE NOISE MYTH:

### SOUND TRAVELS EASILY IN A TIMBER FRAME HOME

Another myth about timber frame homes is that they are noisy. Anecdotes are legion about being able to hear people in ground floor kitchens from upstairs bedrooms and through 'paper thin' walls. In reality, the same problem will occur with any timber stud wall clad in plasterboard if no insulation is used between the studs, something that was as common on the first floor of masonry houses as timber frame homes. The Building Regulations now require a minimum level of acoustic insulation to be used in floors and separating walls on a new house to reduce sound transfer. This can be achieved with the simple addition of mineral wool insulation in the voids. Performance can be improved further by using fibre-reinforced plasterboard, which is far denser than conventional plasterboard, and also stronger, eliminating the problem of fixing heavy items to timber frame walls.

*Building Regs requiring more insulation between floors means there is no more noise in a timber home than in any other*

## THE DESIGN MYTH:

### I'D LIKE MY HOUSE TO LOOK LIKE A TIMBER FRAME HOME

A conventional panel timber frame will be entirely concealed behind external cladding and plaster and will, therefore, be visually indistinguishable from a masonry-built home. Almost any style of house can be built in either masonry or timber frame. The only real exception is a post and beam frame home. As the frame remains a visible feature of the house, it has a big influence on its character. An internal post and beam frame home will only affect the internal appearance of the house. The structure of a house built using a traditional 'half-timbered' oak frame will, however, remain visible both inside and outside the house. This kind of construction gives a new home tremendous character and can suit both traditional and contemporary styles.

Blockwork is Britain's most popular building material. Here it is used with an external skin of bricks

Blockwork can be used with all forms of interesting building shapes, including more modern schemes

# BUILDING WITH BLOCKS

**The humble block is still the cornerstone of the UK building scene. Mark Brinkley explains the pros and cons of using blocks**

The block was an innovation in the years between the two World Wars. It came about as a direct result of the rapid industrialisation of cement production and the widespread adoption of concrete. Before World War I, house walls were routinely built in solid brick, bound together with lime mortars – a method which had held sway since the start of the Georgian housing boom in the 18th century.

The move to cement and cement-based products brought about significant changes:

• Concrete foundations replaced brick footings.

• Cavity walls replaced solid brick walls.

• Concrete 'breeze' blocks began to be used as the load-bearing wall in cavity walls and on partition walls within the house.

Whilst many people still think of these changes as improvements, the real driver behind their rapid adoption was that they were quicker and cheaper for builders. A standard format of block emerged: it was the volume of six house bricks and this standard persists to this day, in the 215 x 440mm block. Rather than having to be baked in an oven like a brick, these blocks could be simply made by pouring concrete into moulds and, because of their large size, bricklayers were able to build blockwork walls in half the time taken for brickwork. Overnight, blocks became the skeleton of the house, and bricks were reduced to the role of raincoat — where they reside to this day. In Scotland and Ireland, blocks even took on the role of

## WHY DO BUILDERS LIKE BLOCKWORK

**● It's cheap. 100mm-wide blocks can be purchased for between £6 and £8/m$^2$, which is equivalent to ten standard blocks. Almost no other building method can compare with this low entry price. Even with blocklaying prices having recently gone above £1 a block (i.e. £10/m$^2$), pushing the overall cost of a blockwork wall toaround £20/m$^2$, there are no obvious ways of building walls for less.**

**● Blocks are readily available. The builders' merchants are all geared to supplying sand, cement and blocks off the shelf, so there are none of the delays involved in having to pre-order from specialists. Furthermore, all the accessories required for blockwork – wall ties, lintels, cavity closers, cavity insulation – are also readily available.**

**● Blocks are relatively easy to lay. Blocklaying is not only quicker than bricklaying but is also less skilled.**

**● Blockwork is "forgiving". You can build walls off less-than-ideal foundations and smooth out any differences in levels as you work up.**

**● Blockwork is adaptable. If mistakes are made in setting out or late changes.**

Blockwork is the most popular system for DIYers. The self-builders of this blockwork home achieved a low build cost of just £134,000

rain screen as well, albeit dressed with a painted cement render or a stone cladding.

Over the past 80 years, since this major change in building practice came about, many alternative housebuilding systems have been used in the UK and some have achieved significant success. But, with the exception of Scotland, where timber frame has come to dominate, blockwork has remained the most popular method of housebuilding and it looks to stay that way for a long time to come.

## HOW DOES BLOCKWORK AFFECT THE FOLLOW-ON TRADES?

Generally, the follow-on trades like to work with blockwork. It's easy for electricians to surface-mount their cables and chasing in cables and socket boxes is easy, provided the blocks used aren't too hard. Similarly, plumbers have a fairly easy time as well, especially as you can drill fixings anywhere. Finish carpenters like the simplicity of being able to place fixings anywhere. They are not quite so enamoured when the blocks are laid badly: it's easy to build walls that are out of plumb and corners that are not square. What can be seen as one of the great strengths of blockwork – the fact that it's "forgiving" and doesn't require high skill levels – can sometimes be one of its weaknesses as well — it's easy to build block walls badly. The follow-on trades where there are acknowledged problems are plastering and painting. Blockwork tends to settle over its first few years and this movement causes hairline cracking in the plaster. It's generally not serious from a structural perspective but it often leads to homeowner distress and builder call-backs with tubs of Polyfilla and emulsion. The perception is that aerated blocks perform worse than concrete ones, though this is denied by their manufacturers. The housebuilding trade has responded to this problem by abandoning wet plastering techniques and switching over to wallboards, usually stuck onto the masonry background using the dot and dab technique. However, for many people this destroys one of the key advantages of having blockwork walls — namely enabling you to have a wet plastered finish. There are other options: using lime renders – either pure or mixed with cement – can build a degree of flexibility into the wall cover. Alternatively, some plasterers have experimented successfully with adding fibre reinforcement to their cement renders.

## THE PROBLEM OF THE CAVITY

When builders decided to switch to a block skeleton, they were also forced to adopt the cavity wall as a design because the external brickwork was separate from the internal blockwork. Initially, this was felt to be an improvement on the solid brickwork which had been used before: the cavity seemed to be an ideal barrier to stop rain penetration. However, the history of the cavity shows that it has caused at least as many problems as it has solved:

- The outer brick skin and the inner block skin have to be tied together to provide structural stability. This is achieved with wall ties. However, until recently, wall ties weren't required to be stainless steel and they have been prone to rust. Replacing old wall ties is an expensive task.
- The bricklayers inadvertently drop mortar down into the cavity where it lodges on the wall ties, providing a bridge across the cavity for rainwater to flow across.
- Junctions become far more complex, requiring cavity trays to be installed in order to keep the water from trickling down inside the house. Cavity trays are frequently overlooked or installed incorrectly.
- The introduction of insulation into the cavity has also compromised the cavity as a waterproofing barrier.
- The cavity wall is, by necessity, a wide wall, which results in a significant loss of internal floor area.

In summary, the cavity is a troublesome detail which results in a lot of problems and this is reflected by the NHBC's claims records, which put rain penetration through cavity walls second only to foundation failure

*Bricklayers drop mortar down into the cavity where it lodges on the wall ties, providing a bridge across the cavity.*

## PROS & CONS

### BLOCKWORK'S DISADVANTAGES

● **SLOW:** **blockwork is perceived to be a slow form of construction, compared to most of the off-site systems that have been developed. However, it is worth bearing in mind that speed of construction isn't always of paramount importance and that the length of time to build a superstructure using blockwork is rarely more than a few weeks. So although off-site systems tend to be much quicker when it comes to completing the superstructure, the time taken to finish the house is the same whichever method you use.**

● **INACCURATE:** **because blockwork is relatively easy to master, it is often carried out rather badly. It is easy to build walls that aren't plumb and corners that aren't true. Superficially this can be hard to detect, but the inaccuracies often become apparent when it comes to hanging doors or fitting kitchen cabinets.**

● **THICKER WALLS:** **ever-increasing demand for thermal insulation is undoubtedly causing problems for blockwork, as it is not naturally a good insulator. There are no obvious voids in which to place insulation so the cavity ends up having to fulfil two roles, one as a waterproofing detail, and another as repository for insulation.**
**Needless to say, these two demands are in conflict with one another. The alternative is to place the insulationeither inside or outside the wall structure, which works fine but eats up a large amount of space.**

A traditional cavity wall, showing the outer blockwork skin, insulation and internal (loadbearing) blockwork

Blockwork built up from foundations

as a cause of warranty claims. Having said that, it's only a tiny number of cavity walls that result in later problems. Bricklayers build so many that the detail is well understood and the weak points are easily addressed.

## TYPES OF BLOCK

Like most aspects of building technology, masonry blockwork has evolved over the years. Whilst the original 'six-brick' block size is still very common, and the concrete block is still widely used, there is now a bewildering variety of formats and different materials to choose from.

- **DENSE BLOCKS.** As the name suggests, these are heavy and strong and so are widely used in foundations and where strength is an issue. They generally have a smooth surface and are sometimes used fair-faced for internal work. They are, however, quite difficult to cut and they are hard to chase out or make holes in.
- **LIGHTWEIGHT OR CLINKER BLOCKS.** More commonly used above ground as inner skin or partition wall blocks. They are much easier to handle than dense blocks.
- **AERATED BLOCKS.** A Scandinavian innovation, dating from the 1950s, mixes sand, cement and air into a block format which is then pressure-cooked in an autoclave for eight hours. The resulting block is typically 50% air. Aircrete is very light — it floats in water. Several advantages accrue from this: the blocks are much easier to handle (because they are so light); they can be sawn, drilled and cut

very easily; and, because they have air trapped within, they slow the transfer of heat, adding some significant insulation value. Whereas traditional concrete block-making takes place across the country, often undertaken by small and medium-sized manufacturers, aerated block plants require much higher levels of investment and there are consequently only three manufacturers in the UK: Celcon, Thermalite and Tarmac, who own a fourth brand, Durox, which is now used exclusively for larger format blocks.

## THIN-JOINT BLOCKWORK

Because aerated blocks provide some significant insulation value, they were widely adopted by housebuilders in the 1980s when thermal insulation levels were introduced. But the UK housebuilders were slow to realise many of the other benefits that accrued from having such a lightweight building block, which could be manufactured to engineering tolerances. In Germany, masons began to abandon cement mortars and switched to thin-joint glue mortars that further improved insulation levels and were much quicker to lay, especially when combined with large-format blocks. When thin-joint systems were introduced to the UK in the late 1990s, they were already well established elsewhere and the teething troubles had been worked through. Where people have tried them, they report much greater laying speeds and improved accuracy but, in truth, British builders have proven very reluctant to embrace the thin-joint techniques.

Why? They seem to really like the standard 215 x 440mm-format block that works so well with a brick outer skin. Thin-joint works best with much larger format blocks. Switching to using thin-joint also requires a new tool set and some new approaches to wall ties. Over the past few years, blocklayers have been so busy that they have had neither the time nor the inclination to experiment with new techniques.

If you are tempted to specify a thin-joint system on your house – all the aircrete manufacturers now offer one – be sure to select a blocklayer who is familiar with the system. The builder needs to be switched on to thin-joint for you

*When thin-joint systems were introduced to the UK, people reported much greater laying speed and improved accuracy*

## PROS & CONS

### BENEFITS OF BLOCKS

**There are several benefits to using blockwork for your structure.**

- **PLASTERING: If you want a wet plastered finish in your house, you have to use blocks because all the other building systems rely on using wallboards. Having said that, many builders don't want a wet plastered wall finish anymore and go to great lengths to stick wallboards against blockwork walls.**

- **SOUNDPROOFING: comes with the mass. The heavier blocks in particular are very good at providing soundproofing between rooms. However, the key area where people worry about soundproofing within the home is in the upstairs bedrooms and here it is rather more difficult to build blockwork walls. You need a steel beam support or a precast masonry floor.**

- **FIREPROOFING: again, masonry materials are inherently fireproof. However, all other building systems provide perfectly adequate fireproofing because they use inert wallboards.**

- **THERMAL MASS: this relates to the fact that heavy masonry objects absorb heat. This has the effect of evening out the temperature fluctuations in a house. This is particularly useful with passive solar house designs where the energy from the sun shining can be stored in the fabric of the house. In summer, it can also contribute to cooling. Note that in this respect, lightweight aerated blocks are not nearly as efficient.**

Structural Insulated Panels (SIPs) being installed to form the walls of a new home. The process is very quick on site

People like using SIPs because they are inherently efficient with plenty of insulation built in. They are also very airtight

# SIPS

## STRUCTURAL INSULATED PANELS EXAMINED

Are Structural Insulated Panels the future of construction for self-builders? Mark Brinkley explains the pros and cons of this emerging construction system.

What is the best way to build a house? It's a question almost all self-builders ask at the beginning of their project. And in seeking to answer it, a huge number of self-builders become aware of Structural Insulated Panels (or SIPs, as they have become known) — but very few have actually taken the plunge and built homes using them. Why is this and is it all about to change? Will SIPs take over the housebuilding world, or will they remain a green curio; a mere footnote in the British self-build scene? We look at the system and why it might be good for you.

### WHAT ARE SIPS?

SIPs building is sometimes referred to as timber frame without the timber. Like panelised timber frame, it works on the idea of building up wall and roof panels on flat surfaces and then hoisting them into position, in contrast with masonry build systems which build walls up in situ. Where SIPs differ from timber frame is that they gain their strength not from any timber skeleton but from the rigidity of the panels themselves. The SIPs panels are essentially a sandwich: the filling is a solid thickness insulation, and the bread is made of rigid building boards such as plywood or orientated strand board (OSB). These layers are bonded together which has the effect of making the panels extremely robust. In many ways, the technique is similar to how aircraft wings are designed, with two skins wrapped around a lightweight core and then welded together to form a single element.

The advantages are that you create a structure with superb insulation levels, few cold bridges and excellent air-tightness levels. Plus, in the right hands, SIPs have the potential for faster construction speeds than timber frame. The panelised roof elements lend themselves to building rooms in the roof, in a simpler and quicker manner than traditional methods.

Sip are well suited to houses that feature sloping roofs, which can be awkward to insulate using traditional methods

## BACKGROUND

The original experiments with structural panels went on in the 1930s in the USA, working to some designs by the world-famous American architect Frank Lloyd Wright. It was a student of Wright's, Alden B Dow, who first hit on the idea of placing insulation in the core, and he placed extruded polystyrene (made by his family's company, Dow Chemicals) inside the sandwich on a series of experimental houses and offices in Wisconsin in the early 1950s. Some of these structures are still being used today. Following on from this, SIPs houses were built, albeit in small numbers, in a variety of exotic locations around the world and they gained a reputation for being virtually bomb-proof, surviving earthquakes and hurricanes whilst all else around them succumbed.

## SIPS IN NORTH AMERICA

Early SIPs houses were relatively expensive to build and it wasn't until the late 1980s, when the requirement for greater insulation levels first appeared, that a number of small producers in the USA and Canada started using them, chiefly because they valued the thermal efficiency, the air-tightness and the accuracy of assembly.

Since then, the use of SIPs has grown steadily, if unspectacularly. SIPs are seen in North America as a premium building product, giving better insulation levels than the standard on-site stick build methods. A recent survey by the Structural Insulated Panel Association showed that the SIPs market is growing year on year by around 20% and that during 2005, 10,485 single family homes were constructed using SIPs, supplied by a total of 67 manufacturers. In Europe, the take-up of SIPs has been much slower, although they are now being used in many Mediterranean developments.

## SIPS IN THE UK

The UK SIPs industry is still relatively small in comparison with North America but it has been making great strides since the turn of the century. In Britain, the undoubted pioneer is Tony Palmer who began making SIPs panels in 1982. Palmer came from a manufacturing background and was heavily involved in developing cavity wall injection systems. Palmer's business, SIPTEC, alone of the current UK suppliers, offers a range of different SIPs panels. "We have done an enormous amount of testing and refining over the years and we've actually made SIPs out of almost anything you can get hold of." Palmer has concentrated on the polyurethane family of chemicals, which are more expensive to make into SIPs panels, but offers them with a variety of different outer wraps, including a unique spray-on concrete system called SIPCrete which, to date, has mainly been of interest in the Middle East. SIPTEC does a lot of its work to order and can vary the specifications to suit.

Palmer is, however, the first to admit that the company which really kick-started the SIPs phenomenon in this country was Kingspan, the Irish insulation giant who purchased a German polyurethane SIPs manufacturer called Tekhaus in 2000. Kingspan, being a long-established public company, was prepared to spend a large amount of money marketing SIPs and thereby gave the whole idea of SIPs considerable credibility, which has been of benefit to all the other British SIPs producers. Kingspan's Tekhaus has done well in the social housing market but has struggled to get going in the self-build arena as Kingspan chose to sell its panels through a small network of installers, some of whom, frankly, didn't understand the requirements of the self-builder. Several prestigious projects were subject to embarrassing errors and delays. It's a problem Kingspan acknowledges and it has started to address it by concentrating on providing training schemes specifically for its installers.

*"Most SIPs suppliers recommend that you should install a whole-house mechanical ventilation and heat recovery system"*

Another early SIPs panel producer was BPAC, now SIPS Industries, based in Scotland. It has been making an expanded polystyrene SIPs system since 2000 and has been working across the country. Being a small producer, it has the advantage of being involved in both manufacturing and installation and this has enabled the company to build up a considerable bank of expertise over the years.

SIPBuilding Systems in Cheshire began manufacturing a polyurethane foam core panel in 2005. It works with three installers: Build It Green (Dorset), SipBuild (Cheshire) and SIPIt (Scotland).

In 2006, one of the oldest names in the UK kit home market, Custom Homes, started offering a SIPs alternative to its standard timber frame homes. Custom Homes doesn't have a manufacturing arm, choosing rather to concentrate on the design and service side of the business. It is therefore relatively easy for it to change its manufactured offering. Its system, which the company has brilliantly christened CHIPs, is made in Scotland, using an expanded polystyrene panel, and is erected by specialist crews.

Custom Homes will continue to sell houses from brochures, in the same manner as it always has, but now offers people the choice as to how the houses should be built. Steve Hunt, commercial director, comments: "The level of interest has been amazing. There is almost nothing between the two systems, cost wise, and since we started offering CHIPs, almost all our jobs have opted for it."

In many ways, the SIPs market resembles the more mature timber frame market. The systems are not quite interchangeable but there are more similarities than differences. Just as successful timber frame companies have learned the hard way that they needed to do far more than just start up a timber frame factory, and in fact have had to become house designers and custom home builders, so the SIPs businesses are learning that the technology they are making is only a small part of the overall service. If you are looking to engage a SIPs manufacturer to build the superstructure of your house, then you would be well advised to look for one who already has a string of satisfied customers that you can visit and chat to.

# SIP FACTS

● **The main attraction of SIPs building is that it provides a fantastic insulation level built into the fabric. This is particularly attractive for sloping roofs, which have become cumbersome and awkward to insulate using traditional methods.**

● SIPs also offer very good air-tightness levels, seen as an increasingly important aspect of low-energy housebuilding.

● **SIPs companies often advertise the speed benefits of using SIPs. However, there are only marginal speed advantages in using SIPS over the more common factory-built timber frame.**

● SIPs are easily adaptable on site. You can cut holes anything up to 1,200mm wide in the panels without any form of structural support. However, this is not the way to take advantage of factory-built panel systems, and it is also extremely wasteful.

● **Even more than timber frame, SIPs buildings require accurate foundations, ideally ±5mm in level and squareness. If the base is inaccurate, then the panels never fit snugly together and you risk building a loose structure that will not be airtight and may be at risk from water penetration. Employ groundworkers who know what they are doing and who know what the issues are.**

● Watch out for competing claims from SIPs manufacturers. In particular there is a debate about which is the best form of insulation with which to fill the core. The two basic choices are expanded polystyrene, which is much cheaper but requires glue to make it stick to the outer boards and also requires additives to become fireproof, and polyurethane, which is innately adhesive and doesn't require any further treatment, but is considerably more expensive as it has to be blown into the space between the outer boards. Polyurethanes are better insulants and therefore don't require such thick panels, which can be a plus point on smaller homes.

● **Watch out for certification issues. The whole concept of SIPs lies well outside the scope of the building regulations and consequently warranty and mortgage providers like to see some form of third party certification to show that the product is fit for its purpose. A BBA approval is the best recognised but many other forms of certification exist. The key factor to look for is to see if the warranty providers, such as the NHBC or Zurich, have already worked with the particular panel system you propose to use and whether they will be happy to accept it on your scheme. If they will play ball, then mortgages and insurances should follow without any problem.**

● One key point to watch out for is the detailing around the inside and outside of a SIPs panel. Just as with timber frame, it is vital to keep some form of ventilation gap or cavity between the panels and the outer cladding. This enables any penetrating rain to evaporate harmlessly. This requirement is no different to conventional timber frame. However, on the inside, you have to make allowance for service ducting because you cannot run cabling or pipework through the SIPs panels (though some American systems do just this). This service void adds some expense to the overall design and also nibbles away at your floor space. However, it is arguably a much better construction detail than normally employed on timber frame houses where the cables are laid within the actual wall and the insulation is often disturbed to accommodate it.

● **Does a SIPs panel house require a vapour barrier? The short answer seems to be no. Provided the wall/roof is genuinely airtight, then there should be no problem with moisture penetration from the inside. Neither polystyrene nor polyurethane absorb or transport water. However, some more cautious practitioners prefer to install a vapour barrier, just to be on the safe side. This would normally be placed in the service void.**

● Whilst many of the early SIPs panel homes survive in good condition, they don't have a track record stretching back hundreds of years and you will still hear sceptics suggesting that such a structure won't stand the test of time. From what has been learned to date, the one thing that causes problems for SIPs is the one that that causes problems for all other types of building — water penetration. If a building is well designed and well built, then it really shouldn't suffer any problems. If by chance it isn't, then repairs may have to be carried out after a number of years, but the risk is essentially no different to any other form of building.

● **SIPs are designed to make up external walls and roofs. As such, they are similarly priced to timber frame walls and rafters. However, if you continue to use SIPs for the internal room-dividing walls, you run into a cost penalty because you are effectively over-engineering the walls. You can decide to switch to a cheaper wall form, typically timber studwork, or stick with the same external wall profile, if only because of the good acoustic properties of the panels.**

● Most SIPs suppliers recommend that you should install a whole-house mechanical ventilation and heat-recovery system. Whilst airtight houses ensure good energy efficiency levels, they also require some form of managed ventilation. This draws stale air from the so-called wet rooms, – the kitchen and the bathrooms – takes the heat out of them and transfers it into fresh air, drawn in from the outside and blown into the dry rooms. Mechanical ventilation needs to be designed well and integrated into the structure otherwise it can be noisy and ineffective. It's an expensive addition to a house, adding perhaps £3,000 to the overall budget, but it probably makes sense with a SIPs panel house. However, the regulations don't require mechanical ventilation and the standard, cheaper choices are an option.

## USEFUL CONTACTS:

Staylor Design: 01670 521641 www.staylor-design.com; Custom Homes: 01787 377388 www.customhomes.co.uk; SIPs Industries: 01383 823995 www.sipsindustries.com; SIP Build Ltd: 0870 850 2264 www.sipbuildltd.com; Build It Green Ltd: 0870 2000 358 www.buildit-green.co.uk; Siptec: 01234 881280 www.siptec.co.uk; Kingspan Tek: 0870 850 8555 www.tek.kingspan.com/uk; Enviropanel: 0870 284 6244 www.enviropanel.com Structural Insulated Panel Association: www.sips.org

**For a full list of SIPs suppliers and more information visit www.homebuilding.co.uk**

# ICF

## INSULATED CONCRETE FORMWORK: THE FASTEST BUILDING SYSTEM EVER?

Is building with Insulated Concrete Formwork really all it is cracked up to be? Mark Brinkley investigates

If you have ever been to a Homebuilding & Renovating Show, you cannot have failed to notice various stands full of polystyrene building blocks. Maybe you have stopped for a chat and picked up a leaflet, or maybe you've simply hurried on by, but, to date, not that many of you have been brave enough to actually build your houses using them.

However, during the past couple of years, there seems to have been a sea change taking place and the suppliers all report sharply increased sales. Not just to self-builders, but to hard-nosed developers as well. An appearance on Grand Designs, albeit not without its problems, has further projected the whole concept into the limelight. So what are these polystyrene houses all about? Is it now time to seriously consider using them as an alternative to the mainstream choices of blockwork and timber frame?

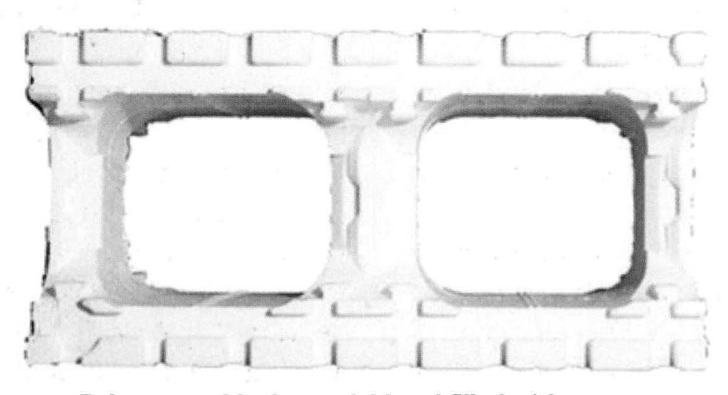

**Polystyrene blocks are laid and filled with concrete**

### INSULATING CONCRETE FORMS

Of course, these are not really polystyrene houses at all. The polystyrene is used as a mould or form into which you pour ready-mixed concrete and it is this concrete that forms the structure of the house. The idea seems to have originated in Germany after the war when they were looking for new methods to reconstruct the bombed-out housing stock. Concrete walls are traditionally constructed using timber formwork, which is taken down after the concrete has set. Timber

This modernist style home in Nottingham was built using Insulated Concrete Formwork

formwork is fiddly to make and a lot of it cannot be reused. Using polystyrene in place of timber effectively kills two birds with one stone: it acts as formwork to mould the concrete and is then left in place to provide insulation for the walls. Hence this building system is known generically as Insulated Concrete Formwork, or ICF.

Whilst ICF is a European innovation, its uptake has been most dramatic in North America. Unlike Europe, North America does not have a tradition of masonry work and if you want a heavyweight structure the options are limited. ICF has thus proved popular for basements and in hurricane areas such as Florida. During the past 20 years, ICF manufacturers and builders have sprung up across the USA and Canada, and most of the systems now available in the UK and Ireland hail from across the Atlantic, often set up here under licence.

In Britain, the first ICF houses were built in the 1970s but they have remained something of a curiosity until recently. What seems to have triggered the recent surge in interest in ICF is the demand for ever greater levels of wall insulation, which is finally causing builders to question the sense in continuing with cavity wall blockwork. The latest changes to the energy-efficiency regulations, which came into effect in early 2006, seem to have accelerated this process further still.

## ADVANTAGES OVER BRICK AND BLOCK

In common with most of the new build systems, ICF is fast to build and requires less in the way of traditional building skills. The formwork goes up with remarkable speed and there are far fewer elements than you get with cavity wall work: no lintels; few, if any, wall ties or cavity trays. Fitting doors and windows is at least as straightforward as it is with masonry work and finishing inside and out is essentially the same. In return you get fantastic insulation levels built in: most ICF systems give a wall U-value of around 0.2, well inside the level demanded by Building Regulations. And ICF systems are flexible enough to allow you to build in any style, to virtually any dimension.

## ADVANTAGES OVER TIMBER FRAME

Timber frame in the UK is primarily built in factories. This is both a strength and a weakness. It is a strength because any structure built under factory conditions tends to be accurate and well made, and on-site assembly is very quick; it is a weakness because in ordering a timber frame you are at the mercy of a factory's production schedule and it may take weeks or even months for the frame to arrive on site. ICF requires two basic components: the polystyrene forms that should be available on most jobs within days, and ready-mix concrete, which is available at a few hours' notice right across the country. Some ICF systems require special fixtures and fittings and on occasion jobs get held up because of unavailability, but in principle ICF is not only fast to build but also does not involve long lead-in times.

## COSTINGS

Perhaps the main factor that turns many potential ICF builders away from the whole idea is their headline cost. They appear to be very expensive when compared with blockwork wall costs. Most ICF systems on sale in the UK cost between £25 and £35/m²; add ready-mix concrete at £10/m² plus a few extras and you have a wall cost of well over £40/m² before you have even taken labour into account. In contrast, blockwork can be built for around £20/m² including labour.

But, as so often happens when you come to cost out elements of building work, a more thorough comparison shows the ICF cost model in a very different light. A blockwork wall on its own is only a small part of the overall wall assembly: it needs an insulated cavity and a waterproof outer skin, usually built from bricks, stone or a rendered second skin of blockwork. Also, the joinery openings require steel lintels over them and there is additional work required with wall ties and cavity closers. A truer figure for the cost of a brick and block wall is between £70 and £100/m².

In contrast, the labour costs on ICF are very low: an experienced ICF crew is capable of laying 5m² of wall per hour. Combine this with an external render coat, costing around £25 or £30/m², and you end up with a wall cost of between £80 and £90/m², slap bang in the middle of the cost range for masonry and timber frame walling.

But in return, you get very high energy-efficiency levels built in at no extra cost, good soundproofing, excellent airtightness and less room for poor detailing, as often happens with masonry cavity wall work.

Another plus factor for ICF costing stems from the speed of build, which reduces the preliminary costs of building, the money spent on fencing, plant and scaffolding. Several of the systems offer the possibility of building the walls up entirely from the inside, thus further reducing the need for external scaffolding until much later in the job. ICF no longer looks expensive and as if to emphasise that point, it is now being taken up by commercial developers as well as self-builders.

## DIFFERENCES

Although ICF tends to be lumped together as if it were one homogeneous product, the reality is that the various systems are very different from one another. They all use polystyrene and they all use concrete but just how they go together varies a lot. Many are based on a moulded block format, such as Beco, Styrobuild and Logix. Others are based around large flat panels that you have to tie together on site: this is how Polarwall, Quadlock and Eurozone work. Others, like Polysteel, use a hybrid system. By and large, the panel systems are cheaper to purchase but require a little more work on site.

The variations reflect the piecemeal way ICF has developed, with lots of relatively small producers working through prototypes to develop their ideal format. You'd be right to infer from this that some systems are more suitable for DIY construction than others and as a rule it is the small-format moulded block systems that the inexperienced find easiest.

*"You get high energy-efficiency levels at no extra cost and less room for poor detailing, as happens with masonry cavity wall work."*

## FOLLOW-ON TRADES

You can clad ICF externally with any material. However, it is true that through-coloured flexible renders tend to work best, as you can apply these directly onto the polystyrene. If you want a brick or stone façade, you have to tie into the structural shell. How you do this varies from system to system: with some there are fixings built in, with others you have to set wall ties through the polystyrene before the pour.

Internally, the walls are routinely finished with plasterboard, stuck on to the polystyrene with sticky dabs. This is very similar to how blockwork homes are finished. Electric cable and pipework can be run within the polystyrene in channels cut with a hot wire cutter.

## INTERNAL WALLS

Internal walls are one area where ICF walls are much more expensive than the industry standard solutions, timber or steel studwork. However, they also produce good acoustic insulation without the need for additional work. And any ICF wall is also a structural wall, capable of taking the load for precast masonry floors. For these reasons, many self-builders specify ICF walls for at least their downstairs internal as well as external walling.

# "WE BUILT USING ICFs"

Despite being a carpenter by trade, Paul Hart wanted to build his and wife, Sharon's, house in concrete and had been checking out Beco blocks for many years at the Homebuilding & Renovating Shows. They got to know Beco's Robin Millar very well: every time they saw him at a Show, they would throw another problem at him, trying to talk themselves out of using Beco. But each time Millar had a compelling answer for them.

Paul commented: "I like Beco because it puts you in total control. I wanted to build as much of this house as possible with my own hands and this system allowed me to do just that. I know it's not necessarily the cheapest way to build a house – the walls have taken 24 lorry loads of concrete – but I didn't want to mess around with subcontractors. I figure if you have to explain to someone how to do something, you might just as well do it yourself."

However, when it came to submitting a planning application, the first architect refused point blank to work with polystyrene blocks because he said they would be a fire hazard. The Harts immediately phoned Millar with this concern. "No, it's alright, it won't burn and it won't melt," said Millar. "For a start, the structure is concrete, not polystyrene and, secondly, the polystyrene is all treated with an additive that makes it completely fireproof." The second architect wanted the Harts to use timber frame, but by now Paul was convinced of Beco's merits and decided to go ahead with the system. "I am really glad we used it: it has been pretty simple and straightforward. For one thing, we were careful about not pouring too much concrete at any one time, just half a storey at once. That minimised the risk of bursts. It also allowed us to build it all from the inside without scaffolding except for roofing and external render."

One issue the Harts feel confused about is heating and ventilating. "We know this will be a low-energy house but that doesn't make it easy to know what type of heating to install, if any. In fact, we have gone for underfloor heating downstairs and nothing at all upstairs, allowing for the mechanical ventilation system with heat recovery to distribute heat around the house. But, in truth, we won't really know if we have too much or too little heating until we have lived through a winter. It would be nice if we could have been specified a complete build package that would have ensured we were getting everything we needed without the expense of over-specifying on things like boilers and heating pipes."

## REASONS TO USE FORMWORK

### IT IS QUICK

**As you might expect with a construction system so brilliant in its simplicity, the structure of houses built using ICF goes up incredibly quickly. There are also far fewer elements than you might get with cavity wall work — no lintels, few (if any) wall ties, and no cavity trays. Taking into account the fact that the structural element of a home's construction accounts for around 30% of the total, self-builders using ICF can expect to save 1-3 months on their project time.**

### IT IS INHERENTLY WARM

ICF houses come with fantastic insulation levels built in — most systems give a wall U-value of around 0.2, which is well inside the levels demanded by the Building Regulations.

### IT IS FLEXIBLE

**While it could be argued that some homes wear their construction method on their sleeve, it is impossible to tell an ICF home from a house built using masonry or timber frame. ICF homes can be contemporary, traditional; curved or straight.**

### TIPS

Although ICF sells itself on its simplicity, it is far from foolproof. There is in fact a fair amount of knowledge needed to build well with it. With all the systems, the concrete pour is an absolutely critical phase. The ready-mix has to be right in order for the concrete to flow evenly throughout the formwork; the support and bracing on the polystyrene blocks also has to be adequate or there is a risk of the walls distorting or even bursting open at pressure points. Mistakes can happen and, because of the speed involved, they can appear to be quite alarming, but an experienced hand can generally fix any mishaps within a few minutes.

In fact Kevin Oelmann, site manager at a Polysteel site, advises others not to be fearful of ICF walls moving around a bit during a pour. "When we first started working with the Polysteel system, we spent almost as long bracing the walls before a pour as we did building them. Then we had a visit from one of the experienced American contractors who showed us how to pour with minimal bracing and then to get everything level and plumb after the pour was complete. Overnight we halved our build speed and improved the finished result."

## DARE TO COMPARE

### ICF VS SIP

**Many self-builders weigh up ICF against SIPSs. Here we compare similarities and differences.**

### SIMILARITIES

- **Both systems use insulation structurally, rather than adding it later to the structure.**
- **Both systems could be categorised as being fast, when compared to their mainstream alternatives, and both demand much less in the way of traditional building skills.**

### DIFFERENCES

- **ICF is wet: the concrete has to be added on site. SIPs are a completely dry method.**
- **ICF is built up on site from pre-formed modular units. In contrast, SIPs tend to be made to order in a factory, like timber frame.**
- **ICF depends on the concrete for its strength: SIPs are inherently strong without adding anything. SIPs, give you a narrower wall profile.**
- **SIPs can't be used for basements whilst ICF can't be used for roofs.**

### USEFUL CONTACTS:

**CONTRACTORS SPECIALISING IN ICF:**

CJ O'Shea: 020 8959 3600 www.oshea.co.uk; Newmil: 0845 090 0109 www.newmil.co.uk; Denstone Construction: 01409 259375 www.denstoneconstruction.com

**ICF INFORMATION:**

The Insulating Concrete Formwork Association: 0700 450 0500 www.icfinfo.org.uk

**ICF SUPPLIERS:**

Beco Products: 01724 747576 www.becowallform.co.uk; Euromac2 UK: 01227 276666 www.euromac2.co.uk; Formworks UK: 01273 478110 www.formworksuk.com; Logix UK: 0845 607 6958 www.logix.uk.com; Polarwall: 01392 841777 www.polarwall.co.uk; PolySteel: 0870 382 2229 www.polysteel.co.uk; Quad-Lock: 0870 443 1901 www.quadlock.co.uk; Styro Build: 01580 767701 www.styrobuild.com Styro Stone: 0871 789 7678 www.styrostone.com

# PROJECT *management*

## BUILDER'S QUOTES

### HOW TO GET A PRICE AND DECIDE WHICH ONE TO USE

You've got planning consent and now you need to get a price from a few builders and decide which one to go with. Michael Holmes advises.

As with most aspects of the building game there is no one way to get a price for your self-build or renovation project. Some builders prefer to give an estimate and will do the job with only a simple written agreement, whilst others will insist on a formal contract with a fixed price quote based on fully detailed tender documents. A lot will depend on the scale and nature of your project, your own preferences, whether you plan to use a local builder or a main contractor, and whether or not you are using an agent such as an architect or surveyor to manage the build on your behalf.

#### OBTAINING ESTIMATES

An estimate is a builder's best guess of what your building project is going to cost, based on what they can see and the information you have provided them with. It may also be referred to as a budget figure.

For a small straightforward self-build or renovation

project, an estimate, written or verbal, can suffice and many small jobbing builders will be unwilling to provide anything other than this. Although it is essential to have the basics of any agreement in writing, there may not be a formal contract. The agreement may take the form of a letter detailing the estimate, the start date, expected completion date and reference to the approved drawings and any specification notes that are available.

The more information you provide, the more accurate an estimate is likely to be. Bear in mind that estimating for renovation work can be particularly tricky, as it is not always possible to assess the extent of reinstatement works required until the project is under way and the existing structure exposed.

You can get an estimate in writing but it is not necessarily going to be the final price that you will pay and so may serve as nothing more than a record of the starting point and the basis from which the final cost is calculated. None the less, it can result in a job completed for far less than it would cost to use a main contractor working to a fixed quote on a formal contract. This is because most contractors will price according to the terms of any contract, allowing for the unforeseen in various ways by marking up costs, and adding to their price to cover any penalty clauses or retentions.

If you are working with only an estimate, it is essential to have a contingency sum available. If costs overrun, you may be able to negotiate, but you cannot pin a builder down to an estimate as a fixed price contract.

Comparing estimates from different builders is all but impossible and no great help in choosing which builder to work with. Instead you should use other criteria (see below) to make your choice.

## OBTAINING QUOTES

A quote is a more binding price for undertaking your building project calculated by a building contractor, or their quantity surveyor, using the information you or your agent provides. A builder is unlikely to be willing to prepare an estimate until you have full tender documents for the building work. Without this information a quote is no more use than an estimate anyway, as it will have too many unfixed variables that could leave you exposed to 'extras'.

Obtaining quotes for building work is also known as

## AND I QUOTE...

### INFORMATION REQUIRED TO GET QUOTES

- A full set of all plans and drawings;
- Specification documents;
- Details of any materials you will be providing;
- Details of any work you will be handling or subcontracting;
- Details of any contract you intend to use;
- Details of any preliminaries;
- The format you want the quote to take.

### WHY QUOTES VARY SO MUCH

- Contractors may vary their mark-up according to how much they need or want the work;
- Contractors make allowances for Provisional and Prime Cost Sums in different ways;
- Labour rates may vary according to the size of the business (PAYE);
- Overheads will be higher for larger firms;
- Some contractors pare their price down and later exploit loopholes in the specification to charge for 'extra overs' that inflate the final price;
- Some contractors use quantity surveyors, others price work themselves;
- Some use measured rates (standard average labour and material prices);
- They may interpret the plans, specification and quantities differently;
- They may include exclusions or other special conditions;
- They may handle 'extras' for variations to the contract in a different way;
- Some contractors work together to create a bias in the process
- Some may include an insurance-backed guarantee in their quote.

inviting or procuring tenders, or an invitation to treat. The documents required by a builder in order to prepare an estimate, known as the tender documents, need to include the following information;

## SMALL PROJECTS:

For a relatively simple project the specification documents might be only a set of the approved plans and building regulations drawings together with the approval notices and conditions, plus information provided by you explaining what you want in terms of lighting, power points, fitted furniture, kitchen and bathroom fittings, floor finishes, etc. You must also include details of any work you will be handling yourself on a DIY basis, or which you plan to subcontract directly, any materials you plan to supply, and any other requirements.

A contractor may be willing to prepare a quote on this basis and to make allowances for any 'grey areas' where there is insufficient detail for them to provide an accurate price. These allowances are known as either Provisional Sums or Prime Cost Sums.

Provisional Sums are items that cannot accurately be priced, such as underpinning and other remedial works. Prime Cost Sums are allowances for items that may not yet have been chosen, such as bathrooms and kitchens, but for which there will normally be a handling charge, labour costs and a charge for project management. The more precise the information you provide, the fewer estimates and allowances will be included and the more accurate the quote will be.

Working on this sort of informal basis, without a fully detailed specification, leaves plenty of room for interpretation and, therefore, requires a degree of trust between you and your builder. Whilst it is legitimate for a contractor to add 'extra over' costs incurred for work omitted from their original quote because of a lack of detail, some more unscrupulous contractors could use this as a way to overcharge and increase their profit. A lack of detail often leads to extra costs and consequently this is an area where disputes commonly arise.

*"Be very cautious of quotes that appear too good to be true – they usually are"*

## MEDIUM AND LARGE PROJECTS:

For a larger and more complex project it is always worth having a full specification document written out by the project designer. This is a written specification that supplements the notes on the drawings and is likely to run into dozens of pages, depending on the extent of the works. It will typically be prepared by the architectural designer and will include a description of the materials, technical standards and techniques that are to be used for each aspect of the build.

In addition to the drawings prepared for the planning application and for the building regulations and copies of the approval notices and conditions, it will be necessary to produce and submit detailed larger scale working drawings of any unusual or individual details that you want the builder to price for. It also means having all of your wiring and lighting plans worked out at this early stage.

A covering letter may also indicate the basis on which tenders are invited including the format the quotes are to take. A standard format is to show each aspect of the work individually, with a breakdown of labour and materials, plant hire and project management charges — the mark-up applied for project management. It may also indicate how allowances such as Provisional Sums and Prime Cost Sums should be treated, to make it easier to calculate actual costs later. Having a common format creates transparency and enables different quotes to be compared on a like-for-like basis.

It is also necessary to indicate when the works are to be commenced and completed, working hours and days, and what form of contract is to be used. There are several standard contracts available, including the range of JCT Contracts (Joint Contracts Tribunal) that are widely acknowledged. Most standard contracts include a retention clause, and some also choose to include penalty clauses for late completion and incentive clauses for early completion.

The tender documents must also make clear who is responsible for preliminary costs, such as site access, security, storage, WC facilities, rest facilities, provision of water and power, site insurance, warranty cover, etc.

Finally, the documents must make it clear if you plan to subcontract any of the work directly to 'nominated subcontractors' or to handle any work on a DIY basis. The contract needs to identify who is to be responsible for this work should there be any defects or delays, and how the implications of this in terms of delays and additional costs are to be dealt with.

## COMPARING QUOTES

The competitive tender process is designed to encourage building contractors to keep their margins down in order to get work and to help you find the contractor who is going to do the work to the required standard, to schedule and for the least cost. This is fine in principle, but in reality comparing different quotes and drawing any useful conclusions can be incredibly difficult. For this reason your selection of a builder should not be based solely on the price quoted for the work and certainly should not be made by choosing the lowest quote.

*"The more precise the information you provide, the more accurate the quote will be"*

Quotes may take a different format that makes it very difficult to compare individual aspects of their pricing — some may even refuse to provide a breakdown of their quote. Your job is to try and unravel all of this and to make sense of it.

Ideally you should aim to get at least three different quotes for your project. To achieve this you will probably have had to identify at least a dozen potential builders and have invited at least seven or eight to tender —several will probably not respond depending on how busy the industry is.

Each quote then needs to be assessed in its own right, and you need to assess how complete the price really is and how many areas there are where the price is not firmly tied down. You can do this by working through each aspect of the project and comparing how each builder has priced for key items. It is probably best to ignore items that have been priced with a Provisional Sum and instead compare the measured rates which they have been used to calculate

## DECSICION TIME

### SELECTING A BUILDING CONTRACTOR

**From the contractors on your shortlist that have submitted a price, the most appropriate to undertake your building project is not the one that simply produced the lowest quote or estimate. It should be the one that scores highest across the each of the following measures.**

### CHOOSE THE CONTRACTOR THAT HAS THE FOLLOWING:

- **A competitive price (having analysed the quotes);**
- **A fair and reasonable approach to variations and extras;**
- **An understanding of your objectives;**
- **The availability you need;**
- **Relevant experience;**
- **Good references from clients and suppliers;**
- **The workforce and contacts needed;**
- **Willingness to agree payment terms that suit you;**
- **Willingness to work on the basis/contract you require;**
- **The guarantees you need;**
- **VAT registration if you want to use concessions.**

these sums. These are the rates they will employ to calculate the final cost for, say, underpinning work.

Once you have analysed each quote, possibly with the help of your agent, and chosen one or two that look both competitive and realistic, you can start to go back and try to negotiate on different areas where you think one may have charged considerably more than the others. Some people choose to commission a quantity surveyor to produce an independent cost assessment on their behalf, and this can be a useful tool to use in negotiating prices with a contractor where large sums are involved.

## WORKING ON A COST PLUS BASIS

An alternative way to work with a contractor is on what is known as a 'cost plus' or 'open book' basis. This is essentially very simple: the contractor charges labour, materials and plant at cost and then adds an agreed mark-up, usually 10-20%, for managing the project. Sometimes labour is charged at a flat day rate for simplicity and there may also be a day rate allowed for their own attendance on site.

This is a very transparent way of working, because in theory everyone knows exactly how much everything is costing, including the cost of the contractor. From the client's perspective: they see a work schedule showing labour charges that they can cross check, plus invoices for all of the materials and hire charges etc. They can be confident that they are not being overcharged and that there is no incentive to cut corners or to compromise on the quality of materials. It also ensures that any extras for variations or unforeseen work are being charged at the same rate as the rest of the contract.

From the contractor's perspective: they know that they can be entirely open about costs and what they are charging for their own time, and that regardless of what changes the client requests, or what unforeseen work arises, they will still make their mark-up of 10-20%.

*"You could to go back and negotiate on areas where you think one may have charged more than the others"*

The disadvantage of working this way is that it is based largely on trust. In particular you must trust the contractor and his team to work efficiently and not to drag the job out and inflate labour costs, and to only charge for materials used on site. On this basis it may be a good idea to have an independent agent acting in a supervisory role, making random checks and signing off invoices for payment. This will carry a cost, however, and the benefit and peace of mind needs to be weighed up against the additional cost.

Another criticism of working in this way is that you do not have a firm quote for the work on which to base your budget and cash flow requirements. Typically the contractor will give a budget figure, which is his best guess but not the final price.

Working on a cost plus basis can be ideally suited to renovation projects, and particularly restoration projects – where an old building is being repaired and updated – as much of the work will be priced on a Provisional Sum basis anyway. Despite this, most advisers will feel that they have to recommend against working this way because of the inherent risks. There are standard contracts available for working in this way with an agent available from JCT.

## AVOID THE CHEAPEST QUOTE

It is always wise to be very cautious of quotes that appear too good to be true — they usually are. If a single quote is well under the others, it is likely either to have omissions, or the contractor may be planning to make up the difference once they have secured the contract by exploiting loopholes in the specification and tender documents, or by overcharging for any variations you later make to the contract — it is very rare for people to make no changes, so it can be hard to avoid this!

Bear in mind that whichever quote you accept, a builder is unlikely to be prepared to make a loss on a project if it ultimately turns out that they have under-priced the contract. They will look to recover at least their costs, if not their profits and this can lead to disputes. It is far better to have an accurate and realistic quote in the first place. ●

# HOW TO FIND A BUILDER

## FINDING AN HONEST RELIABLE TRADESMAN

**Mark Brinkley searches the internet to see if discussion forums or building organizations are any help in the quest for good value builders**

Wouldn't it be good if there was a website where you could check out tradesmen? Just where do you go to find a builder who is honest, reliable and good value? Isn't there some published blacklist of cowboy builders?

In recent years, several organisations have had a stab at addressing this issue, promising to build up a database of competent contractors, simultaneously weeding out the rubbish. To date, none of them has been conspicuously successful. None has achieved a critical mass and there isn't a website that I would immediately point people to.

At the end of last year, John Dough posted a message on the Homebuilding & Renovating discussion forum, inviting readers to find and rate various builders throughout the UK and Ireland. The site, www.ratethebuilder.co.uk, is designed to be community-powered and hopes to provide "a way to rid us of cowboy builders". I checked it for my area and it hadn't generated any traffic at all – there wasn't even a list of builders, let alone rated ones. This remains a major stumbling block for such ventures: without information, they have no traffic and without traffic they have no information. And even if they do get good information, it tends to go stale quickly.

There are some well-run professional sites around, the best known being www.homepro.co.uk. This business started life during the dot.com boom at the end of the 90s with the aim of logging just about every jobbing builder in the land. But that proved an impossible task and its business model is now far simpler. It provides insurance-backed guarantees on the work of around 5,000 vetted contractors, who each pay an annual fee to HomePro plus a small premium for a ten-year guarantee. It mirrors what the long-established Federation of Master Builders does with its 12,000 members and the www.findabuilder.co.uk website.

The problem with this filtering method is that it is self-selecting. These are not organisations run by consumers for consumers; they exist primarily for

the benefit of their membership and are as much about marketing as they are consumer protection. That's not to say that their members won't provide an excellent service and the guarantees aren't well worth having — it's just a move away from the simple idea of rating builders.

Then there are the Government's attempts to get involved. It feels that it should be its job to champion consumer protection in an area which causes tens of thousands of complaints each year. Trouble is, it really doesn't have a clue how to do it. Its first attempt, QualityMark, was unsuccessful. It launched in 2000 and required members to pay 0.75% of their turnover to them in order to be vetted and then to be allowed to display the QualityMark logo. As most building firms are doing well if they turn 5% of their turnover into useful profit, this was never going to catch on. It hardly attracted any builders at all and was laid to rest in 2005 and replaced with Trustmark at www.trustmark.org.uk, regarded by many as QualityMark-lite.

Trustmark makes no attempt to vet builders and build up a database of the good, the bad and the ugly – it simply acts as a portal which directs you to other sites, like the FMB. If you want to become a Trustmark-registered building firm, you have to be checked and vetted by one of its approved scheme operators. In other words, Trustmark's job is to vet the vetters, not the builders themselves.

Which brings us round full circle. The reason that there isn't an authoritative, independent website where you carry out your own vetting is that it is a hopeless task. There is something like one and a half million people earning their living from construction in this country. The vast majority of them are capable of doing good work, but almost all of them will have also experienced nightmare jobs. A builder who claims never to have had a job go bad is quite simply a liar. How could you possibly break down this constantly changing kaleidoscope of human endeavour into a few simple categories? I don't think you can. Builders don't divide neatly into good guys and cowboys anymore than their customers do.

So, it's back to square one. Recommendations. Reputation. Pub gossip. You will never beat getting your ear close to the ground and finding out who is good at what and who is available and looking for work. Hiring a builder is, and always will be, a risky business, which no amount of vetting will ever entirely eliminate.

# GET THE BEST FROM YOUR BUILDER

## WORKING WITH YOUR BUILDER NEED NOT BE DAUNTING

The secret to a good working relationship with your builder is being a good client, says David Snell.

Building your own home puts you in a position of complete responsibility and for many this first taste of real power can be a daunting task. Whilst knowledge of the technical aspects of building, or at the very least the sequences of events, is useful, what is undoubtedly of far greater significance to the successful self-builder is the ability to handle people and situations. Acres of print are devoted to choices of materials and the selection of suitable contractors, subcontractors and architects. But very little is devoted to the qualities that the self-builder should bring to these partnerships.

Many of the practices and attitudes of the factory floor or office do not easily translate to the building site. The engineer who boasts an ability to work in micrometers and looks forward with eager anticipation to "teaching these guys how to do things properly" will almost certainly come a cropper. The self-builder who stands like a factory inspector, clocking people in and out, will soon find themselves with an empty site.

There's no need to be a bad client, however, and if you follow a few simple rules and guidelines you can get the best out of your builder by getting the best out of yourself.

### UNDERSTAND YOUR BUILDER'S PROBLEMS

Why should you worry about the problems that those you employ experience? Because if their problems impact upon your site, you will suffer in the end. Whenever a builder quotes for a job, they do so on the basis of certain assumptions. Usually there is enough 'fat' in the price to cover for unknown eventualities. Sometimes things will not be quite as presupposed and if the changes are minor then you would be right to think that a decent tradesman should shrug them off. But make a distinction between somebody 'swinging the lead' for a bit more money and somebody who is faced with something major that they and you could never have envisaged.

In the end you want your project finished and you want it done properly. If the unforeseen problems mean that a respectable tradesman or contractor has no alternative but to walk away from the job, then that's not going to help. If they decide to stay but are forced to skimp on the work then that's no good either. A contract is a contract and you could insist upon its fulfilment — and you'd be perfectly within your rights. But you can't force people to work and any attempt to do so might be more expensive than renegotiating. If that all sounds like a recipe for financial anarchy, then you are right — if, and only if, you fail to spot the difference between genuine hardship and somebody just trying it on.

Any builder is only as good as his last job. That's why when you've made all the checks, you need to keep abreast of things. Look for warning signs. Look for lack of attendance, materials not arriving on time or subcontractors failing to turn up. They might be warnings of financial difficulties, or they may just be personal difficulties. Is it the self-builder's job to worry about the marital problems of his builder? Of course it isn't — in the sense of becoming a marriage guidance counsellor. But if sympathy with their problems and a willingness to step into the breach and take over – albeit on a temporary basis – some of the site management, means that your site keeps going, then it's well worthwhile.

*Don't be afraid to stop and ask. It pays to make full use of the experiencce and knowledge of the professionals*

## GET YOUR CASH FLOW RIGHT.

Many builders work with an overdraft that would eclipse most self-build mortgages. Builders regularly get into financial troubles, not because they are technically insolvent, but because their cash flow is so bad. In reality it is probably something to do with the job before yours or the job before that. But here again, if you made the in-depth enquiries at the beginning, this might be something that you know about.

Be that as it may, it's important for you to get your cash flow right and it's vital that you have the money available at the right time if you're going to keep continuity on site. Most subcontractors will want paying in cash at the end of the week. If you haven't got it then they'll not be there on the Monday and will slip off to another job where they think or know they'll get paid on time.

A positive cash flow is the principal advantage of the new generation of 'advance' mortgages available within the self-build lending market. But even with these mortgages it is important for the self-builder to exercise restraint and to watch out for overspending. Running a building site is like running a business and if you do nothing else, then careful management of the finances, by means of a running check on a daily basis allied to a meaningful cash projection and programme, are essential.

## BE WILLING TO LISTEN AND TO LEARN.

Most self-builders are entering a new field. Even experienced self-builders might have something to learn and, indeed, most builders and subcontractors are on a constant learning curve with new regulations and methods coming on stream.

As the self-builder you are the instigator and the final arbiter of everything that happens on site. You chose the site. You chose, with the help of the architect and the planners, the design. You chose the materials and the specification. So here you are on site with men who have done all this for years and who know far more than you do about how it all fits together, and they're asking you what to do!

Don't be afraid to ask for advice. If a subcontractor asks you whether to do something one way or another, then they might just be testing you or they might just be aiming to show you how knowledgeable they are. If you don't know the answer, answer with a question, "I'm not sure. What would you normally do?" Almost invariably they will have the solution on tap and the 'problem' will be solved. If not then ask around. Maybe the warranty inspector will know. Almost certainly the building inspector will have a view, as will your architect or designer. Don't be afraid to stop and ask. Building a new home is just about the most regulated and overseen activity there is and it pays to make full use of all of the experience and knowledge of the professionals.

## DON'T DITHER – MAKE UP YOUR MIND.

Nearly all jobs that run over time get blamed on the builders. Yet in many cases it's the clients who are at fault. Simple changes of mind during the job can add days onto the schedule. Altering things once or twice might be accommodated but if you make a habit of it, the sequences – and with it the relationship between the parties – will pretty soon break down.

Knowing the sequence of events through a build is important. You need to know when things that you are choosing or are undecided upon are going to be needed and you need to equate that with the delivery times from order (see H&R Aug '05 for a full project planner). It's no good getting to the point where the kitchen units are needed only to have to tell the builders that they'll be several weeks more. The whole job will come to a grinding halt. Make your mind up in good time.

*"Believing that you and the tradesmanare an equal partnership is a mistake. Its your project, not theirs"*

## KEEP A SENSE OF PROPORTION/HUMOUR.

Most self-builders will find themselves spending money in amounts and at greater speed than they have ever envisaged. The project can take over lives. At times it might even seem that nothing is more important than this new home.

Keep a sense of proportion. It is important but is not more important than family life and it certainly shouldn't be more important than your business life. Don't make the mistake of believing that you and the tradesmen are an equal partnership. This is your project. It's not theirs. You'll enjoy the house afterwards. You'll reap the benefit of any increase in equity. For them it's just another job. Talk of partnerships is naïve and if you try to involve them in such talk, they'll pay lip service to the concept, laugh at you behind your back and take advantage of your obvious inexperience.

It's not always going to go right. Things will go badly at times. Be prepared for them and keep things in perspective. Very few things that go wrong on a building site spell absolute disaster and most can be remedied. The solution may soak up your contingency fund but that's what it's there for. It may eat into your projected equity increase but it's unlikely to swallow it up entirely.

## DON'T SWEAT THE SMALL STUFF.

Most people don't know one face of a brick from another. Then they come into self-building and they're faced with a myriad of choices. They make those choices and then they defend them zealously against any attempt at change. But building houses isn't like that. Too many other interested parties are involved and if you insist on getting 100% of what you want, rather than the 80%, which you're likely to get, you'll be disappointed.

Be pragmatic. If the planners don't like your choice, then be prepared to compromise. If the bath taps that you've set your heart on fail to turn up on time or cease being manufactured then there are thousands of alternatives, most of which are probably just as good or even better.

Be aware that a failure to compromise can be very damaging to the entire concept. Always keep the bigger picture in mind, which is finishing the project as a whole and on budget. Details, which seem important at the time, will always pale into insignificance with the passage of time.

## INSIST ON A BASIC AGREEMENT

All of the advice that you'll see in writing usually exhorts the self-builder to enter into a written contract with whosoever they chose to employ in any capacity. Architects and package deal companies will probably not be prepared to proceed other than on this basis. But there is no doubt that the vast majority of building contracts between self-builders and builders, and self-builders and subcontractors, proceed with no formal contract other than perhaps an exchange of letters.

For some this is an anathema. They cannot countenance the idea of not having a long and formal document detailing every part of the contract. Perhaps they are right. Perhaps if things go wrong they'll be covered and if it goes to court they'll win. But will it be a Pyrrhic victory? Perhaps the person who carefully manages things, who pays for nothing that is not done and approved of, has the edge?

Certainly the heads of agreement need to be set down somewhere and if no formal contract is employed then at the very least there should be 'offer and acceptance' in writing. But the pragmatic self-builder will very quickly realise that there are many competent builders and subcontractors who would run a mile from sheaves of paper or formal-looking documentation.

Of course, if everything goes right on the site then any contract is just waste paper. It's only if things go wrong that it's needed and the main point of need revolves around just what to do if things go wrong, how they'll be sorted and what arbitration process will be used. The self-builder needs to be able to negotiate and may need to be prepared to calm the irrational fears. Be aware that insistence on a contract might mean a builder either pulling away from the potential job or, perhaps worse still, inflating the price to cover for supposed problems caused by it. This is where the simple contracts, such as the JCT Building Contract for a Home Owner/Occupier come into their own (see www.jctltd.co.uk for more information). These are only a few pages long, written in plain English to cover all of the major details with most of the points dealt with by simple tick boxes. Another option is the free contract from the Federation of Master Builders, downloadable from their website at www.findabuilder.co.uk.

*"Joining in with the builders as one of their mates can just as easily lead to advantage being taken"*

## KNOW WHEN TO PAY.

A self-builder should make sure that they have the money available for the job and they should look to and manage their cash flow in order to keep things running smoothly.

But there is another side to this and that is that as well as paying on time, they should learn not to pay too much up front. Basically the rule should be never to pay for labour in advance. At times there may be circumstances where expensive materials need to be purchased by builders or subcontractors and they might admit that they haven't got the money. Don't make an advance payment. Purchase the materials yourself and that way the title in the goods will be yours.

Always try to be 'in hand'. If you're using a builder then the payments will be made in arrears on the completion of set stages and as long as both parties keep to the agreement then there is very little to go wrong. If you're using subcontractors and the job is estimated to take 10 weeks then divide the quoted sum by 12, not 10, and make that the weekly draw, thus providing an incentive to finish and a reason to do things right.

## BE AWARE OF SNAGGING.

Perhaps the biggest bone of contention for anybody moving into a new home, whether self-built or not, are those relating to snagging or the putting right of things that go wrong. The only difference is that with self-builders it is they who must put in place the correct mechanisms to put things right.

Many think in terms of retention clauses. They work well with the bigger and more reputable builders. They work very badly with smaller builders who will often

agree to having them in the contract, add them to their original worked-out figures and then discount them, assuming that they are never going to get them.

It's all about relationships but more than that it's about money. Snags that are obvious before completion can be put right before final payments are made. But snags that appear six months later, as they almost certainly will, are not that easy to accommodate without a formal retention or agreement for the builders to come back. Those building with subcontractors may choose to carry out later snagging themselves because, almost certainly, most subcontractors will not agree to a retention. On the other hand, most reputable plumbers and electricians will agree to come back for little or no charge if faults arise. In the end, for most self-builders, the most they can do is insist on things being done properly in the first place and accept that in six months time they will have to redecorate.

## KNOW YOUR PLACE.

Building sites are not terribly formal places. Keeping the relationships on a strictly formal basis might work in some instances but it will engender hostility in others. On the other hand joining in with them as one of their mates can just as easily lead to advantage being taken. Be friendly but always keep that little bit of reserve. You're not one of them. This is their job but it's your project. You may need them again, presuming you're satisfied with their work and you might make good friends. But never lose sight of what it means to be a good client — it will be the defining factor in getting the most out of your builder.

# ON TIME *on budget*

## HOW TO GUARANTEE PROJECT SUCCESS

David Snell explains how to manage your project so that you move into your new home on schedule — and without going over budget.

### CHOOSE THE RIGHT ARCHITECT/DESIGNER

Self-building is all about informed choice. When you choose the person to design your new home it is important that you choose someone who is of like mind and who will listen to what you want. If they insist on you having what they think is best and will not countenance you being involved in the design, then they are the wrong person for your project. On the other hand, you don't want someone who will slavishly go along with ideas that they know from experience are fundamentally wrong. What you want is a balance — somebody who expresses what you want on paper, yet brings experience and knowledge to the table to temper your wilder ideas and reach acceptable compromises.

### BE TOUGH BUT FAIR WITH BUILDERS AND NEVER PAY IN ADVANCE

If your builders or subcontractors fail to perform, either in terms of agreed timings or in the required quality of the work, make sure that you let them know your concerns. If at all possible write to them or, better still, get your architect to write to them setting out clearly what is wrong and just how and when you expect things to be put right. Make it clear that future payments will be dependent upon their compliance. Never pay in advance. With builders, agree stage payments and do not make these until the stage is reached and the work is completed to a satisfactory standard. With subcontractors, divide their quoted price by the number of weeks they will be there and split the payments up such that you always have money in hand.

### DON'T MAKE THREATS YOU ARE NOT PREPARED TO CARRY THROUGH

Many self-builders are inexperienced when it comes to the building industry. You don't have to be an expert on building to successfully complete a self-build project but you do have to be good at managing situations and, in particular, people. If you make a threat to, for example, hold back payment until such time as bad work is rectified and then fail to carry it out, do not be surprised if things go from bad to worse. The law should always be the final option, not least because if the builders are bad enough to warrant such recourse, they are probably 'men of straw'. If there is no other avenue, bite the bullet and instruct solicitors. Often that, and the resulting letter, proves sufficient to bring about a resolution.

## MAKE SURE THAT YOU CHECK OUT THE GROUND CONDITIONS AND ANTICIPATE FOUNDATION COSTS

Apart from elective extras at the later stages of a self-build project, the most common reasons for cost overruns are in the ground. If there is any doubt about the ground conditions, organise a full soil investigation and commission a foundation design.

Never just hope against hope that things will be alright. If you have to change foundation type in mid-build, then the abortive work will have to be paid for. Not only that, but the work carried out in error might well increase the cost of, and exacerbate, the difficulty of building the new foundations. Check with the local authority building inspectors regarding ground conditions. They will have seen many different excavations and will know local ground conditions. If they have any doubts or suspicions, follow this up with a thorough investigation. No checks can offer 100% proof and the only site investigation that is going to be precisely right is your actual excavation. Prudent planning can iron out uncertainties and prevent abortive work, however.

### SAVE MONEY — BUT DON'T SKIMP ON KEY MATERIALS

If you use cheap bricks then your house will look cheap for as long as it stands there — and in time it could cost you, or whoever buys it from you, more money in maintenance.

The roof is perhaps one of the most important features of the home. Not only does it protect your home from the elements but it defines its status and value; similarly with the windows. These things are not easy to change. Once the choice is made you are, to a large degree, stuck with it. If money is tight, think in terms of getting the best prime materials and perhaps having cheaper fittings and fixtures, including kitchen units and sanitaryware. These can always be swapped for better ones at a later date. Mix and match. Buy cheap kitchen units and slightly more expensive worktops and you might find they look better than high priced furniture. Mix cheap wall tiles with expensive border or dado tiles.

## MAKE SURE YOU SEE SAMPLES OF EVERYTHING YOU HAVE CHOSEN – IN PERSON

Looking at things in a brochure is no substitute for seeing the article in the flesh. Bricks can look completely different in real life. It does not always do to get samples as bricks vary and they also look completely different in the wall. Ask where the bricks have been used and go and see them there. Brochures for taps and sanitaryware are designed to show the goods in the very best light. Look at them in real life. Feel the baths and sinks. Check for rigidity and finish. Check taps for a smooth action. Kitchen units might look good in the showroom — but under lights that are brighter than anything you will have in your home.

Take sample panels home and study them for a few days to be sure of your choice. If what you get on site is not what you thought it would be like, then you have only yourself to blame.

### DON'T BE AFRAID TO CHANGE YOUR MIND — BUT DON'T KEEP ON DOING SO

If you find that you have made the wrong decision about anything, stop. Wait until you have all of the information and then start again. If you decide that the person working for you, be they a bricklayer or an architect, is not giving you what you want, you have made the wrong choice and need to stop and move to terminate your relationship as quickly as possible. If you have doubts about the design and its cost effectiveness – if you are not sure that it is the right thing to be building there – stop and re-think before it is too late. Once you have started work, it might be acceptable to change your mind once or twice. But if you come home every night and change what has been built during the day, the costs will explode, the time taken will extend beyond reason and your labour will very quickly get fed up and may even leave site. Plan your build to avoid too many changes by thinking ahead.

*"For the builder this is just another job, however much input and enthusiasm they are prepared to put into it"*

### FIND A BUILDER WHO IS SYMPATHETIC TO YOUR GOALS

You should always be on the same wavelength as anybody working on your site. The architect should be your partner in coming up with the design of your choice. In a similar vein, the builder should be as one with you in executing and achieving the goal of your new self-built home. Be aware that for the builder this is just another job, however much input and enthusiasm they are prepared to put into it. For them, this is the way they make money. One day your project will just be a memory and they will be onto the next client. For you this is not just another job — this is your job. You are going to have to live with it. Balancing those two positions is the trick to a good working relationship.

## BUILD AS BIG A HOUSE AS YOU CAN AFFORD

House price inflation has not gone away entirely and property prices and values consistently outstrip other forms of investment. Build as big a house as you can afford. If you can't afford to build it completely as you would wish, get planning for a bigger house and design it so that it can be built in stages, as your finances improve. Consider leaving off the garage for the time being, even if you do choose to build the footings or purchase some of the external materials at the same time as the rest of the house. If you have a small site, increase the size of your house by building a basement or putting in attic trusses. If your finances don't permit it then leave these spaces as voids until such time as you can afford to fit them out.

## DO YOUR RESEARCH AT THE PLANNING OFFICE

Of all the people and bodies involved in your new home, it is the planners who are perhaps the most important. They determine whether or not you are going to be building at all and if so, what your new home is going to look like. Visit the planning office yourself. Don't trust information to third parties. Read about the local planning policy and study the local plan/ framework. Talk to the planning officers about your proposals and get a clear – first hand – idea of what their criteria are. They will only want to talk about a specific site and proposals; they won't want to talk about hypothetical ideas. Make a note of their suggestions. If they draw or doodle any sketches to illustrate what they are talking about, get copies so that you can show them to your designers. Keep the discussions friendly — you have a long way to go and if it starts off with bad blood it won't get any better.

### GET THE NEIGHBOURS ON SIDE

Whenever proposals for a new house or houses arise, all sorts of people object — especially neighbours. Quite often their objections are quite spurious. They are understandably worried about the impact that the new house is going to have on their amenities and, above all, the value of their home. Remember that these people are going to be your neighbours: when the new home is ready you are going to have to live alongside each other. Without doubt their lives are going to be disrupted by your building works. Wherever possible, move to placate neighbours. Talk to them about your proposals and see if you can address their concerns. If they are on side it will speed your planning application. If they are not resentful they may actually be very helpful during the build, especially in terms of security

## MAKE SURE THE SERVICES ARE IN PLACE

Check the position and availability of services. As soon as you have plans of your proposals available, send them off to all of the service suppliers for a quotation for supply. Check the lead-in times and make any payments on time. When your application is accepted, keep on top of it. Check with the suppliers at regular intervals that the work is still on schedule. Make sure that the relevant trades know when they are coming and that everything that needs to be done on time is done. If suppliers have to reschedule work, it can add weeks to the project.

*"In most cases it does not make sense to spend more than the completed property is worth, so keep a tight check on costs"*

### MAKE SURE THAT YOU COMPLY WITH PLANNING CONDITIONS

All planning consents have conditions upon them. Read these carefully. Some of them are standard but they are nonetheless important. A condition relating to the timing and expiry of a consent is vital. If there is a condition on an outline consent requiring application for Approval of Reserved Matters (detailed consent) within a certain period, make sure that the time has not elapsed. Where work has already started, make sure that all of the conditions have been satisfied, especially those that require something to be done or agreed prior to commencement of work. Make sure that conditions are capable of being satisfied. Visibility splays might need the agreement and legal co-operation of neighbours. Conditions limiting the occupation of a dwelling might put off lenders, meaning most self-builders should steer clear.

## CALCULATE END VALUES

Profit may not be your motive for self-building. You may just want as much as you can get, to your own specification, for as much as you've got. But in most cases it does not make sense to spend more than the completed property is worth. Keep a tight check on costs. Check the addition of land purchase price and building costs against the estimated value of the completed house. Take the plans to a local estate agent and discuss end values with them. If they seem phased by the plans and don't seem to be able to comprehend what the finished article will be like, then move on to another agent. Be prepared for them to be conservative on value at this point, before the full impact of the proposals are in the flesh. Allow for that factor in your calculations but do not allow yourself to be over optimistic. Assess end values by reference to similar properties that are up for sale or have been sold in the area.

### MAKE ALL OF YOUR DECISIONS IN ADVANCE

Do not be led by events. A common factor in successful projects is the ability to think and plan ahead. Study the plans carefully. Imagine the completed house. Make sure that the doors are all hung on the right side and swing the right way for your occupation and your furniture. Choose materials well in advance of their requirement and check lead-in times and delivery requirements. If those lead-in times start to stretch, investigate alternatives. If unforeseen and unavoidable problems or set backs occur, stop and think carefully. Plan how you are going to move forward from that point and how you are going to regain control.

## MAKE SURE YOU SET A BUDGET, INCLUDING A CONTINGENCY

The prudent self-builder will always set a budget and, having done so, keep a running check on how things are proceeding relevant to it. When preparing a budget, check on labour prices and research material prices and the various options. As the spend progresses, keep a running tally of gains and losses. If one thing costs more than expected, be prepared to trim something else to stay on budget. Set aside a contingency sum of between five and ten percent of the build costs. If this does not get used up in the foundations or construction of the weathertight shell then by all means relax a little and start to think about whether you can afford those extras that you had hoped for.

### MAKE SURE YOU HAVE ENOUGH CASH FLOW

Many builders have overdrafts that would dwarf most self-builders' mortgages. If you are building with subcontractors or small builders then they will expect and need payments to be made on time, simply in order to carry on in business. If there is a delay that is their fault then they will have to deal with the consequences but if they properly reach a stage where the work has been done and money is due, then their ability to keep continuity on site might be compromised if it is not forthcoming.

*Prepare a programme and work out your cash flow in advance. If the budget is tight then the chances are that so is the cash flow.*

Prepare a programme and work out your cash flow well in advance. If the budget is tight then the chances are that so is the cash flow. If there are 'pinchpoints' then anticipate these and move, in advance, to warn contractors and assure them that the money will be available. Do not keep them in the dark. The relationship will deteriorate quite quickly if they are expecting money that simply fails to materialise. If necessary, make alternative financial arrangements or consider short term bridging finance. Get funding arranged in advance – once you are in crisis it may be much harder to secure.

## DON'T BE TOO BULLISH ABOUT YOUR OWN INPUT

Make sure that you are capable of carrying out what you plan to do. Once a building project starts, money will be going out in almost unimaginable amounts and timescales. If you are planning to do some of the work yourself, or undertake a complete trade, then make absolutely certain that you know what you are doing, that you have the necessary skills and capabilities and that, above all, you have the time to do it. For you, this project might seem the most important thing in the world. For the other tradesmen it is their livelihood. If you are going to put a brake on progress such that it affects their take home pay, relations on site will break down.

Taking on the role of project manager might seem financially advantageous. Letting that management slip and failing to anticipate events and requirements on site might turn your taking on of this responsibility into a false economy.

### DON'T TRUST KEY DECISIONS TO ANYONE ELSE BUT YOURSELF

Those who simply buy a developer's house off the shelf have every right to spend the whole of their occupation bemoaning the design, the workmanship and the specification. Those who self-build have decided that they want to have their choices and not those of somebody else. Why then leave important choices to the architect or builder? Their choices may well be right as far as the structural integrity is concerned but that does not mean that you should be excluded from the decision making process. Whether to have attic trusses, underfloor central heating, hard or soft plaster — these are decisions that affect your lifestyle just as much as the more superficial things such as kitchen units, baths and colour choices. Make sure that it is you who makes the final decision, under advice.

## LINE UP SUBCONTRACTORS IN ADVANCE AND KEEP THEM UP-TO-DATE

Once work commences it will be necessary, if continuity

is to be maintained, for subcontractors to be available when needed. Sometimes this requirement is within the day but at other times it might be to within the hour. Subcontractors don't just do one job, they have many different jobs on the go at any one time and the measure of a good one is their ability to keep continuity on them all. To do so they need reliable information. Keep them advised of progress on site. Check their availability. It is not easy to change horses mid-race but if you are racing to get to a stage and they have indicated that they will not be available either slow down or investigate the possibility of getting alternative subcontractors. Remember that this is your project. It doesn't do to go around upsetting or letting people down but in the end, it's your project that must come first.

### CHECK OUT THE LEGAL BITS

Your solicitors will be concerned to check out everything they get to make sure that you have a good title. However, it is most unlikely that they will ever visit the site. Make a note of all dimensions. Check these against the title plans and carefully measure the site to check that there are no ransom strips. Check on site to see that no part of the land has been encroached upon by others, possibly leading to an adverse possession. If other people's or bodies' services or drains cross your land, make sure that this does not impact upon your proposals.

## ASK QUESTIONS

Knowledge is power. Don't be blinded with science. Don't allow architects, tradesmen or anybody else to leave you confused about what exactly they are talking about. If you do not understand the terminology, stop them and ask them to explain. Get them to show you what they are talking about. This is your project — you have the right to know. If you are being sold something, ask to speak to others who have had experience of the product. If you are thinking of employing somebody, ask them for the names of people they have done work for before and then go and see those people and ask them whether they did the work properly and on time. Above all ask if they were helpful. Read all you can about self-building. Join the discussion forums and pool your knowledge with others in the same situation. They will be able to share tips and may also be able to solve problems as they come up. Seek out other self-builders and compare notes on suppliers, architects and tradesmen.

### GET A WARRANTY

If you want a mortgage on your self-build project you are going to need a warranty. Even if you do not want or need a mortgage, if you ever want to sell, the chances are that whoever wants to buy will need a mortgage. If the property is less than ten years old, their building society will then ask for details of any warranty and, if there isn't one, then although it is not impossible to find ways around the issue, the sale could be put in jeopardy. A warranty equals peace of mind. Not only do you have a piece of paper that certifies that your new home is built to an acceptable standard but you will know that, during the build process, someone is inspecting on your behalf and making sure that things are designed and built correctly and that materials conform to certain standards. Even if you have a supervising professional, such as an architect, certificating the work, it still pays to have a warranty because, in most cases, any responsibility only exists between you and the architect and does not extend to future purchasers.

## GET YOUR PLANS SORTED OUT — IN DETAIL

Plans and specifications can be as detailed as you like but in a self-build project, where the self-builders are the ones making the final choices and decisions, some things cannot be decided upon at the plans stage. Identify these 'grey' areas and make the necessary decisions in good time. If your builders are not sure on any aspect and you have not made the necessary decisions, they will almost certainly take the easiest, cheapest and least physically arduous option and that might not accord with your wishes. Avoid having to have work undone — it is expensive, time consuming and demoralising for all parties.

MOVING FORWARD
HOT
abstract
bright red
detective

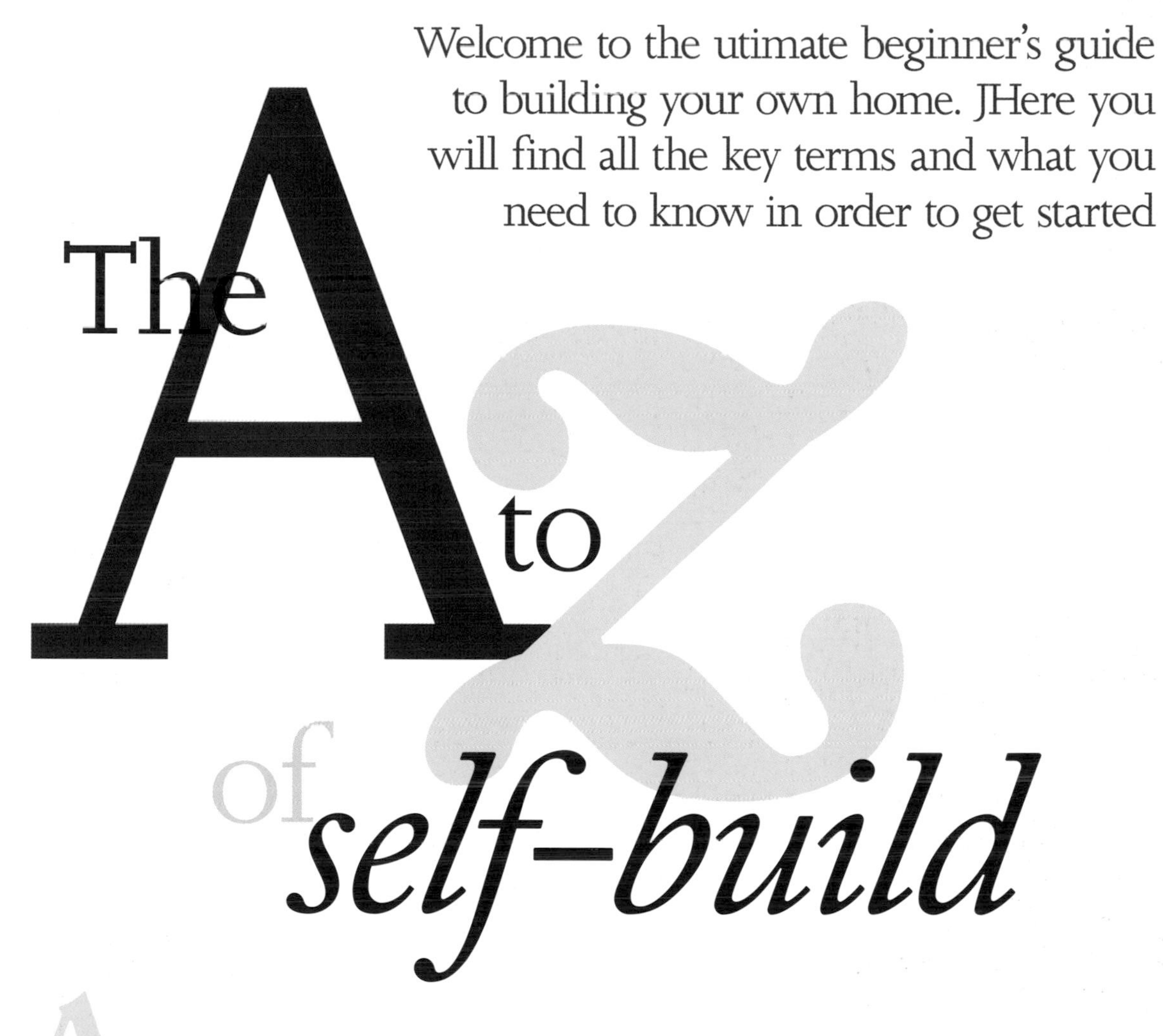


Aa

## ACCESS

Direct access from a highway is the most fundamental element that turns a bit of land into a viable building plot. Your local Highways Department will take a keen interest in your intentions after being consulted at the planning application stage and will offer guidance depending on the category of the road you require access on to. You should of course have made contact with them before submitting your planning application.

If the road is an A road, for instance, their requirements are likely to be much more stringent than if the plot was on a rural country road. Issues such as the ability to access the plot without the need to reverse out, the position at which gates are set back from the road, and visibility splays – namely, the measured angle at which you'll be able to see oncoming traffic – will all have to be dealt with. Any change to your access plans after planning permission has been granted will need to be approved again by the Highways Department.

## AIR CONDITIONING

Traditionally thought of as an unnecessary luxury in most UK homes, recent warm summers have seen air conditioning for the home become increasingly popular in top-end designs. Although conventional suppliers (whose units work similarly to a fridge, but without the box) rely on expensive (to install and run) one-off electrical units – the sort of thing you might see at the window in a New York apartment – some suppliers are offering a slightly more sophisticated system as an upgrade option on whole-house mechanical ventilation systems. Don't forget, too, that an underfloor heating system can be utilised for comfort cooling — check with your supplier for details.

Basements are increasingly popular with self-builders and are used for a variety of uses, from games rooms to home cinemas

## ARCHITECTS

A house designer can only call themselves an 'architect' if they are registered with the ARB (Architect's Registration Board) and are a member of RIBA (Royal Institute of British Architecture). They will have completed seven years of training and usually offer both design and supervisory services, usually for a percentage fee (between 8-12% of the complete build cost). Although many architects don't design individual houses – involvement in larger commercial projects is much more lucrative – you can easily find architects who specialise in one-off designs through ASBA (Associated Self-build Architects). Architects are far from the only option for getting a design — consider architectural technologists, package companies or freelance designers. Whoever you work with, make sure you have thought through your own requirements, have seen previous projects the designer has worked on, and establish a clear understanding of fees early on in the process.

## BASEMENTS

The UK has for a long time lagged behind the rest of Europe and North America in the provision of basements in new homes. The increased pressure on space, however, mixed with the growing number of tight and often sloping sites means that this is beginning to change.

While much of the building trade remains nervous about basements – due to anecdotes of flooding in large part – there is no doubt that the growing popularity of the basement in UK housing is due partly to the development of several prefabricated solutions, often from Europe.
The key to success is to properly waterproof the structure – most often with an external membrane – and install adequate ventilation, light and drainage.

Although basements have a reputation for being expensive, given a standard site they can usually cost between £500-700/m². This low-sounding figure is partly due to the fact that they are rarely fitted out with the expensive finishings that contribute so significantly to above-ground costs, such as kitchens. This figure means that including a basement level on a regular four bedroom detached home will cost between an extra £25-50,000.

Basements are particularly worth considering on sloping sites, when much of the structure will need to built anyway, to ensure levels above ground. This form of 'semi-basement' will have a much less dramatic impact on your overall costs.

## BEAMS

A beam is a structural element that carries a load, most common in housing as a flooring structure. The beam will transfer the force down into vertical supports, such as posts or block walls. If you want to create a room that is wider than average

Beams carry the weight of the floor above, and in this instance have become a feature in their own right

(4m or so) then you'll need to begin thinking about specialist beams, such as steel (rolled steel joists, or RSJs) or engineered timber, such as 'glulam'. Whether or not you'll need special beams is entirely down to your designer working in collaboration with a structural engineer.

## BEAM AND BLOCK FLOORING

As its name suggests, a form of floor structure that combines a number of evenly spaced precast concrete beams, infilled with building blocks. It's a fast, relatively cheap and solid form of flooring structure that is supplied nationwide by several specialist companies, basing their plan on your design drawings. The floor is then usually screeded over. They are popular within the building industry as they are fast to install and provide an immediate safe working platform.

## BOILER

Your boiler – the vessel which heats the water around your house – is one of the most important purchases you will make during your project. Boilers are rated according to the energy they can produce and, therefore, you will need to calculate your home's heating requirements (ask a plumber, or available shortly at www.homebuilding.co.uk) before going shopping. Typically, most new homes will require a boiler operating at between 20-30kW. There are, however, many options to choose from. A combination (or combi) boiler has a second heat exchanger which effectively provides instantaneous hot water — meaning the hot water system doesn't require a cylinder for hot water storage. They are highly convenient, particularly for smaller installations. Traditional system boilers require an auxiliary cylinder for the hot water, which is stored ready for baths and showers etc.

Boilers are also measured by their efficiency — i.e. how much of the energy going into the boiler is turned into useable energy in the home. A boiler, even 15-20 years old, is likely to operate at no more than half the efficiency of a brand new model. As of 2005, the Building Regulations require all new boilers (either new build or replacement) in the UK to be rated at least 'B' on the SEDBUK scale (i.e. at least 80% efficiency), while many of the leading condensing models operate at over 90%.

Boilers are increasingly being designed for maximum operating efficiency, with many models now being 'modulating' – operating between a range of outputs according to demand rather than simply on/off, which means they have to work much less hard – while others offer weather compensation devices to regulate output according to the latest temperature outside.

Expect to pay between £1-2,000 for a quality condensing boiler.

## BRICKS

There are thousands of bricks to choose from – at the cheapest end the 'engineering' bricks that you might find on low-cost public sector projects (costing less than £200/1,000) and at the top end handmade clay bricks (at over £1,000/1,000) – and the key to success is in finding a brick that suits your design and surroundings. Using a typical 225mm-brick, budget for 60 bricks per square metre. A typical house has between 130-200m$^2$ of facing to cover. Bricklayers tend to quote based on the whole wall – i.e. not taking into account window openings – so you'll end up paying for a few m$^2$ you won't need, although the bricklayer should build in the frames around the openings.

A successful brick facing is one of the things that so few mainstream housing developers get right and is an essential skill for self-builders and renovators to master. Look at the differences in the stock and note how – particularly for those wishing to create a traditional look – older houses tend to use a range of different shades. Try creating your own mix or looking at manufacturers' special mixes. Your bricklayers will need to pay just as much attention to the mortar (which makes up 20% of the overall facing) and the bond itself (i.e. the pattern in which the brick is laid) in order to

Bricks range in price from 20p to over £1 each

get the perfect look.

It's worth knowing that brick merchants operate a practice known as 'brick registration' which means that the first merchant you contact will take your details and register you with them, meaning that they benefit from a commission from the suppliers and you can't buy from elsewhere. It pays to use your builder contacts to circumvent this problem.

## BROWNFIELD SITES

The term 'brownfield' has been around since the early 1990s and is a piece of planning jargon used to describe sites that have been previously used in some format — either for industrial, commercial or residential use. The current official definition of the term classes domestic gardens as brownfield, which is why so many gardens now contribute to the UK's supply of building plots. In general terms, planners are much more minded to grant permission for building on a brownfield site than they are on a virgin greenfield site. The Government is keen to create land for up to 60% of its 3 million homes target on brownfield sites.

## BUILDERS

A builder will be the person that organises the construction of your house — they are also known as the 'main contractor'. Builders may in actuality do little on-site building work but most small-sized firms, which dominate the industry, tend to operate as a small team of subcontract labour managed by a single contractor who manages the schedule. It goes without saying that a good builder is key to a smooth project, so look for recommendations from local building sites or homes that have recently been completed, check out industry associations such as the NHBC and FMB, and always check previous work in person. You can circumvent the requirement for a builder by managing the project yourself (see Project Management).

## BUILDING REGULATIONS

A series of documents that ensure all new construction projects meet pre-designated standards. In England and Wales, the system is lettered – so that Part 'L' of the regulations refers to Thermal Efficiency, Part 'M' to Disabled Access and so on – whereas in Scotland they are numbered, so that Section 1 relates to Structure, 5 to Noise and so on.

While it is possible to work 'on notice' which means that you can merely give notice of intention to start work before commencing, the safer route is to submit your detailed building drawings for approval by your local Building Control department before starting work. They will then ensure the plans meet the requirements and carry out stage inspections to check up on the project. Building Regulations inspections have been privatised since the Building Act of 1993 which means that several approved bodies can also handle your project.

## BUILDERS' MERCHANTS

For those self-builders buying their own materials – don't forget that many builders will buy their own as part of a self-build contract – a close relationship with a local merchant is essential. You'll be able to negotiate a standard discount as a member of the trade and operate an account, which will give you useful credit terms of either 30 or 60 days on all purchases — a real help with cashflow. Choose a merchant based on the range of their stock and guaranteed delivery turnarounds, but also visit several in your area to assess their understanding of your project Many will operate a quotation service (for a modest fee) which will give you prices upfront as a take-off from your building drawings.

## BUILT-IN VACUUMS

A built-in vacuum enables the homeowner to simply plug the vacuum pipe into one of several outlets around the property. The benefits of installing a built-in vacuum over using a typical mobile cleaner are that it is practically silent

– the motor is usually located in the garage – and that it is more efficient, because of the lack of need for a filter. Finding somewhere to store the pipe is the main disadvantage. Ducting needs to be fitted at first fix stage and a system should cost between £400-1,000.

## CAPITAL GAINS TAX

UK taxpayers enjoy exemption from Capital Gains on their Principal Private Residence — meaning that you won't be liable for tax on the profits from any future self-build. Likewise, homeowners wanting to build themselves in – or sell-off – their garden for development, enjoy exemption as long as the whole is not more than half a hectare, and the garden was continually part of their Principal Private Residence.

Serial self-builders – those who build a house, move into it and start building again almost instantly – are in theory not liable for CGT as long as they can prove that they were not using self-build as a form of income and that all the profits from their sales went into the next property. Contrary to popular opinion there is no set time limit for staying in a house to enjoy exemption. You'll simply need to prove that you were living there, so it's worth keeping utility bills.

## CARPENTERS

There's much confusion between the definitions of a carpenter and a joiner. Put in its simplest terms, a carpenter is someone who makes and repairs things from wood, while joiners apply wooden objects in houses — dealing with things like doors and windows. Therefore, if you wanted something making from scratch in wood, you'd need a carpenter; if you wanted someone to fit a staircase or hang doors, you'd need a joiner.

Chimneys can be an important architectural feature

A close relationship with the local builders' merchant is essential

A good builder is the key to a smooth contract

## CHIMNEYS

It's far from a necessity these days to have a chimney – a minority of commercially built developer homes bother – but if you want an open fire then chances are you'll have to have a high block- or brick-built chimney. As with most parts of a home these days, there are several precast fireplace, flue and chimney options, designed to ensure correct draw from the fire (dependent on factors including the size of the fire and the size of the room it's in), all of which enjoy significant take-up in the self-build industry. Feature chimneys are a highly desirable feature of new homes and an elaborate design with handmade bricks in different patterns and clay pots can add up to £1,000 to your build costs.

## COMMITTEE (PLANNING)

Decisions on submitted planning applications are either placed in the hands of planning officers ('delegated powers') or – more likely with new individual homes – made by the local authority's planning committee. Committees will also make the decision on any application that is subject to objections (for instance, from neighbours). Planning committees consist of local politicians and it is perfectly legal to lobby them in favour of your application. Committee decisions are made at (usually monthly) planning committee meetings, and applicants are often permitted to speak for a set period of time.

## CONCRETE

To ready-mix or to mix on site? Concrete will be an essential part of your building project — used by the cubic metre for foundations and floor slabs. The traditional mixed-on-site ratio of concrete is 1:3:6 (cement: sand: gravel) which is used for foundation mixes (in ready-mix terms known as GEN 1); this strengthens to 1:2:4 for a floor slab mix (ready-mix GEN 3). Your ready-mix rep will be able to provide you with a suitable mix for specific jobs.

For any significant building work, ready-mix, brought on the back of a truck carrying 6m³, is the best option. Expect to pay in the region of £50/m3. A concrete pump makes a big difference to speed of application and when combined with one of the self-levelling concretes can make filling foundation trenches a half-day job.

## CONTRACTS

A contract is absolutely no guarantee that things won't go wrong between you and your builder and while it provides the extra chance of getting something back in the event of a dispute, there is little benefit in trying to force a reluctant builder to sign one. In most cases, a detailed written specification of the work to be carried out, along with an agreed price, in writing, should suffice. The most self-build-friendly of all the building contracts is the JCT Minor Works Contract — it's cheap and easy to use.

The essential things to clarify with a builder are what you expect to get in return for the money you are paying — and when you intend to pay. The best way to make this as watertight as possible is to be as detailed as you can with the specification from the start.

## CONSERVATION AREAS

An area specially designated by the local council as one with 'special architectural or historical interest, the character or appearance of which it is desirable to preserve or enhance.' In practical terms, this places an extra level of bureaucracy on all planning applications on homes within the area and means that changes to buildings (for instance, replacement windows) that would not otherwise require planning permission now do so — they have to be approved by the local conservation officer.

The common interpretation of the definition of a Conservation Area means that many self-builders and renovators are under the impression that contemporary designs would be unlikely to gain approval in these areas. In actual fact, many conservation officers prefer to see contemporary schemes as they are deemed more respectful to the existing architecture, being obviously different rather than a weak interpretation of traditional styles.

## DESIGN AND DESIGNERS

A well-considered house design is the starting point for any successful self-build or renovation project. Come up with a build cost budget and ensure that it's your realistic budget, rather than a fantasy wish-list of architectural features, that informs your design. The H&R Average Build Cost Guide, published every month in the magazine, will give you an approximate cost/m2 for your new house, and this should give you general guidelines as to what size of house you can afford.

At this stage it is also worth coming up with a rough outline brief, which should include your room requirements, general thoughts on an overall style, and your priorities in terms of features — a large breakfast kitchen, dressing room, open plan interiors, etc.

From these criteria, you can approach a designer. Interview several — this is probably the most important appointment of the whole project. Designers come in all shapes and sizes (see section on Architects).

Your can commission a designer to

either simply provide you with basic drawings for planning and Building Regulations requirements, or to help you supervise the entire project and appoint a builder.

Once on site, ensure that you stick to the design, and if you have to make any changes, agree them clearly with anyone working on your house. It often pays to have somewhere to post up the latest set of official drawings on site in order to avoid any confusion.

In theory there's nothing to stop you coming up with a set of designs yourself, probably using one of the wide range of CAD packages currently available for PCs. However, be aware that planning officers (and committees) often inevitably judge a house's merits on the quality of the submitted drawings – it's a visual exercise, after all – and you'll need to be convinced that the application looks its best, particularly on sensitive sites. Additionally, it's very rare for self-builders to be fully abreast of all the Building Regulations requirements, not to mention be confident enough to come up with 'builder-safe' technical drawings, so most self-builders end up using home design software packages for playing around with ideas, if at all.

## DIY

Great money-saving idea or fallacy? The answer is probably somewhere in between. Thanks to changes in the Building Regulations there are less things (particularly parts of plumbing and electrics) that self-builders and renovators can do themselves these days. It's also fair to say that the DIY involvement of

Front doors are an expensive feature but need to work well with the overall style of the house

an amateur on a professionally run building site can slow down the pros around them and end up having a negative effect. Only around 5% of self-builds are truly DIY to their maximum extent and while they are usually exceptionally cheap (e.g. around or less than £500/m²), they take much longer than a professional job. When considering DIY, take into account the money you could be earning by working extra hours at your regular job, and be honest with yourself about the quality of the finish you'll achieve.

## DOORS

Your external door should be chosen to fit in with the overall style of the rest of the house and will most probably be hardwood, as it is deemed to be less prone to movement and warping than softwood. Alternatives include GRP and even steel. Expect to pay from £150 upwards for a hardwood door. You should budget around £100 for an internal door.

This front door is an integral part of the architectural vision for this entrance

## DRAINAGE

Getting rid of the excess water that your new home will create is not terribly sexy, but it is certainly an essential part of your project. As most existing mains sewer systems can't cope with additional rainwater loads, you'll need to come up with separate runs for the foul water (household-generated waste) and the rainwater (sometimes referred to as storm drains). Drains should be laid at gentle falls at least 600mm under the ground. Assuming you can connect to the mains drainage, expect to pay around £40/m run for each type, meaning that on a typical house it's wise to budget around £3,000 for a complete setup, including labour. You'll also have to pay a standard infrastructure charge in England and Wales, currently £245.

Councils are increasingly insisting that rather than allowing your rainwater to drain off into the mains system, you install a 'SUDS' — a sustainable drainage system. A SUDS involves a variety of techniques

The main driveway choices are tarmac, block paving or chipping

broadly equivalent to a permeable landscaping scheme – an update of the old soakaways – ponds, ditches and so on.

If you are nowhere near the mains sewage system, an 'off-mains' solution is necessary.
**See Also Off Mains.**

## DRIVEWAYS

There are plenty of choices for materials when it comes to driveways. Whatever you choose, you'll need to lay 150mm of hardcore, preferably over a membrane to allow water to pass through but prevent mud and vegetation doing the same. Tarmac is arguably the cheapest option. H&R Contributing Editor and author of The Housebuilder's Bible, Mark Brinkley, calls this 'The Wild West of the Building Industry', and as a result prices – and quality – can vary enormously. Expect to pay around £10/m². Likewise, gravel is a cheap option that can be particularly attractive – there's also a wide range of finishes available – but it will need to be laid properly (three or four layers, each one rolled and left for a day at a time) in order to avoid sinking.

At the other end of the scale, block paving is a good option, particularly for smaller driveways. Expect to pay around £20/m², while top-end options such as granite setts can cost double this.

In most cases your builder should be able to lay a basic drive, but driveway work is also carried out either by specialist firms or many landscaping outfits.

Don't forget that you'll also need to create an access to the main road with a drop kerb. A standard job should cost £200 or so.

The good news for self-builders is that, assuming it is part of your approved planning application, all driveway work will be zero-rated for VAT purposes.

## DRY-LINING

A term used to describe the method by which plasterboard is applied to timber or metal frames, replacing the traditional 'wet' plaster arrangement which involves the plaster being applied straight onto blockwork. It is increasingly common in new homes thanks to advantages of it resulting in a dry finish much quicker than the conventional route. Some plasterboards now come with a smooth ready-to-paint finish that means self-builders can do away with the usual requirement for a skim coat over the top of the board. Expect to pay around £1.50/m². Boards come in standard sizes of 1,200mm x 2,400mm x 12.5mm, but there are plenty of variations.

## FIRE SAFETY

Standard one or two storey homes will be affected by the fire safety section of the Building Regulations in marginal ways. There is a requirement for the fitting of smoke alarms on each storey, as well as 30-minute fire doors for rooms connecting to a garage, in addition to a means of escape window on all habitable rooms above ground floor (it's called an egress window and the opening dimensions need to be at least 450mm x 450mm). However, it's when you're building a third storey, or carrying out a loft conversion, that the fire safety regulations really begin to kick in.

Crucially, you'll need to ensure

that the main staircase in the house should directly lead to the front door via an enclosed hallway — open plan designs are problematic. Additionally, the walls and doors onto the staircase need to have a 20-minute fire rating, and any floor structure should be resistant for 30 minutes. Your Building Control officer will be able to advise in detail.

## FIRST FIX

Any work involved in the running of services (electrics and plumbing) around the house carried out behind the plaster. A well-considered plumbing plan will ensure pipework is concealed where possible.

## FLOORING

Your choices for internal flooring are much more varied than they used to be. Despite its apparent fall from the heights of its 1980s popularity, carpet is still the preferred choice for most self-builders (particularly those with families) and it's easy to find a range that fits in with most styles, both contemporary and traditional. Wooden and stone flooring, however, is the real success story in recent years. Wooden flooring can either be engineered (in which a layer of the wood is bonded to a usually MDF core — the basis of the click 'n' fit type of floor) or solid planks, which tend to be more expensive. Budget at least £20/m2 for a quality engineered floor and £30/m² for a solid hardwood floor (materials only). If you're intending to install underfloor heating, the safest option is to opt for an engineered floor (it won't move like

Stone flooring is a popular choice in kitchen areas where spills and stains are a regular hazard

a solid floor might) but you can get round the problem — talk to your underfloor heating supplier.

Stone comes in all shapes and sizes — current favourites include slate and limestone (or its cheaper and more widely available alternative, travertine). It's fantastic over underfloor heating and costs between £20-50/m², again materials only.

## FLUE

A flue – the means by which exhaust fumes escape from the house, either from a boiler or a fire – is a surprisingly complicated choice.

The important thing to understand is that all flues require some form of intake of air to get them to expel the fumes outwards and upwards. A conventional flue relied on ventilation through the house, but as homes get more and more airtight, balanced flues, which draw air in from the same opening through which the exhaust fumes are expelled, is the preferred option.

Exposing the flue gives an almost industrial look to interiors

The size and height of your flue will depend on the output of the heat source — your supplier will be able to give detailed guidance on the requirements.

## FOOTPRINT

The external dimensions of the house. The footprint is different to the method often used in the housebuilding world, which is gross internal floor area: the sum of the room sizes and internal walls, discounting external wall space.

## FOUNDATIONS

Foundations need to be dug according to a predetermined plan, and to have been accurately surveyed and set out. It is surprising just how often this is not done, and occasionally the ramifications can be very serious indeed, as completed houses turn out to be in the wrong place and subsequently have to be demolished. Your plans should

The cost of foundations varies hugely depending on ground conditions

Garages can be integral, detached or, as in this case, attached

identify all the load-bearing walls and the width of the trenches to be excavated. The depth of excavation is harder to predetermine and this is routinely decided by the building inspector on site. This is where things can get a little bit tricky, because if you have a difficult site, the foundation trenches may have to go down two metres, sometimes even more, below ground, which is expensive and potentially dangerous.

What your building inspector or warranty provider is looking for is principally a good bearing on solid ground. However, you can never be certain just what lies beneath the ground until it's opened up. This has led to professionals becoming more and more cautious about foundations and specifying lots more concrete or, increasingly, engineered or piled foundations. It's a difficult task to present foundation costs in a simple manner because each site is different and the ways foundations are built can vary a lot. However, on simple sites with straightforward issues, the foundations (which include excavation, concrete, blockwork and the ground floor) should cost around £100/m² of footprint. Thus a 100m2 bungalow might expect simple foundation work to cost around £10,000. Note that this amount doesn't alter for two or three storey houses, one of the reasons that they are slightly cheaper to build on a cost/m² of internal floor area basis than bungalows.

## GARAGES

There are basically three types of garage: integral, where the garage forms part of the main mass of the home, and has rooms above it; attached, where the garage is effectively bolted onto the side of the house and linked with an adjoining door; or detached. Where possible, traditional designs aspiring to any sort of style before 1900 should go for a detached option — it's not terribly authentic to try and pretend that period homes needed space for a 20th century invention. That said, a large detached garage can be designed to complement the overall style of the house with careful attention to external materials.

A typical garage will cost between £5-10,000 to construct.

Hh

## HEATING

Divided into two elements for new homes — space heating and hot water. Almost all homes will require a boiler to produce both; while some of the leading eco-friendly schemes incorporating high levels of insulation, passive solar design, as well as microgeneration can possibly

Underfloor heating – plastic pipes laid into the floor structure – is a popular option for self-builders

remove the need for space heating from a boiler, that still leaves the requirement for high-temperature hot water — the demand for which is significant, particularly in family households.

Heat can be emitted through underfloor heating, skirting heating, warm air or, more conventionally, radiators, and in order to choose a boiler you'll need to work out your family's heat requirements in kWh.
**See also Hot Water, Boilers**

## HEAT PUMPS

A heat pump is a device that moves heat from one place to another. It can be used to make things either hot or cold and it is the technology built into all the world's refrigerators and air conditioning systems. In the past 50 years, scientists have been perfecting ways of using heat pumps for domestic heating and, after many years as a green curio, heat pumps are looking to become a mainstream option for home heating, especially where mains gas is not available.

There are two factors behind this. Firstly, the technology has become far more robust: the early versions were unreliable and often failed to deliver as promised. Secondly, the cost of heating oil and liquid petroleum gas has skyrocketed, causing people to think much more seriously about other options. The heat pump, and in particular the ground source heat pump, appears to be a major beneficiary.

Heat pumps are a hybrid heat source. They are run entirely on electricity but they capture additional energy from the external environment, most commonly heat from the garden space around the house. They take a few degrees from this low-grade heat and transfer the energy into a smaller volume of water at higher temperatures inside the house. The efficiency of heat pump systems is measured by the coefficient of performance (CoP). This is the ratio of units of heat output for each unit of electricity used to drive the compressor and pump for the ground loop. Typical CoPs range from 2.5 to 4. The critical factors determining the efficiency of the system are the performance of the heat pump itself and the input and output temperatures: the narrower the range of temperature between the source and the house, the more efficiently the system runs. However, heat pumps continue to work effectively even at sub-zero temperatures.

## HOT WATER

The traditional system was for a cylinder to heat water, fed by a tank in the loft, through copper pipes inside. As the hot water never passes through the boiler, this is known as an indirect system. Typically this will include a back-up immersion heater.

An increasingly popular system these days is for an unvented system, which means that there is no loft pipework for expansion as it can store hot water at mains pressure. The leading name in this field is Heatrae Sadia, whose popular Megaflo provides balanced hot and cold water supplies and high flow rates, perfect for power showers.

Other options include a thermal store, which uses a cylinder of hot water to heat cold water channelled through it at mains pressure. It, too, gives high flow rates of instant hot water.

When considering your options for hot water, consider the level of requirement for the system, and judge products not just on their capacity, flow rates and cost but also their recovery times — essential in a family home.

## ICF

Insulated concrete formwork is the name given to the form of construction whereby hollow polystyrene blocks (moulds) are formed on site and then filled with concrete. It is responsible for a growing number of self-build homes in the UK although still forms a tiny minority compared to blockwork and timber frame. Despite its simplicity,

this is not a DIY construction technique, but while there have been occasional problems on site, particularly with too much concrete being poured into the moulds and bursting out, it is a highly energy-efficient way to build. ICF houses are incredibly warm and structurally very solid, and the higher materials costs are usually offset by faster build times.

## INSULATION

A means of increasing the thermal efficiency of a wall, floor or roof. The requirement to build thermally insulated homes is relatively new. Before the 1970s, it was unusual to have any insulation built into a house. Many homeowners would place an inch or two of glass fibre matting in their lofts, but that was really as far as it went: there were no regulations demanding anything be done to make a house hang on to its heat. This capability to hang on to heat is called thermal efficiency and it is measured in U-values. The lower the U-value, the more heat you hang on to.

The effect of tightening U-values on energy efficiency is dramatic. A centrally heated house, built in the early 1970s, without any insulation, would consume five times more fuel than its 2004 equivalent. Typical space heating demand has fallen from 250 kilowatt hours, per square metre, per annum, down to just over 50 kilowatt hours per annum. And, by adding still more insulation, you can reduce this heat load demand even further — right down to levels at which almost all the space heating requirements are met by incidental

You'll be required to install a minimum amount of insulation – but exceeding this will help keep down energy bills

gains from the occupants.

## INSURANCE

**What insurance do I need?**

• As soon as the land/site is purchased, Public Liability insurance should be bought. A site owner needs to protect against potential claims from members of the public. Public Liability insurance covers your legal liability for injury or damage. However, don't rely purely on insurance — steps should be taken to prevent/discourage access, taking into account obvious hazards. Are there lakes or pits that should be signposted and fenced?

• Any existing structure should be insured. As well as protecting the owners' interests, lenders require such insurance. As with land, protect the property against unauthorised access, for example from squatters or children, and drain/isolate any mains services.

• Next comes the actual building work and associated materials. A Contractor's All Risk policy (CAR) insures the structure from the first footings to final completion. As the name suggests, this is a comprehensive policy so don't accept exclusions such as storms, as these are the very things a lender will want cover against. The CAR policy also provides cover for materials whilst on site and in transit and can be extended to insure any owned plant and tools. Additionally, specialist self-build policies provide cover for existing structures and caravans/site huts. When hiring plant equipment or tools, check the hiring terms. Hirers may be required to insure the item, as well as making provision for ongoing hire charges, should it be lost or damaged. This can be added to the CAR policy at very little cost.

• If you intend to directly employ subcontractors, Employer's Liability insurance is needed to dovetail with Public Liability cover. Where engaging a firm with its own people, management and equipment, Employer's Liability may not be required. Injury to self-employed persons, friends or volunteers may well present an action against the site owner as an 'employer'.

• Liability insurances protect any legal liability for injury to third parties or employees but they do not insure accidents to the site owner. Incapacitation can affect budgets and timescales — protect against this with Personal Accident cover: it will provide some flexibility.

• Contractor/supplier disputes. If work or materials are substandard and the site owner is in dispute with the contractor, Legal Expenses cover can help speed things up, protecting that all-important budget. Many policies also provide cover for squatter evictions and other legal problems.

Most people opt for a large kitchen these days, with space for eating and living combined

## JOINERY

Your choice of joinery – traditionally incorporating the wooden elements of your house, such as windows and doors, and the staircase – has such a large impact on the overall look of the house that it's critical to not only prioritise budget here but to also figure your choices into the design stage. Windows in particular play a critical role. The choices in joinery now are so much more than just timber — steel and aluminium, and particularly PVCu, are popular choices for windows. It's often said that from a design point of view windows are very much the 'eyes' of the house and it pays to get them right — many self-builders and renovators specify bespoke designs as opposed to off-the-shelf varieties, although, of course, this route is more expensive. Self-builders should expect to negotiate a discount off the list prices from the large joinery outlets.

Joinery finishes – such as the staircase – tend to be built, bespoke, on site

Kk

## KITCHENS

The role of the kitchen in the home has been increased in importance in homes of the past 20 years, with more emphasis being placed by homeowners on using the kitchen not just for cooking but for much more besides. Hence, many self-builders and renovators these days prioritise a so-called living kitchen, which will certainly include room for a breakfast table and quite possibly facilities for more regular dining and simply hanging out – perhaps with sofas and chairs – or doing work on a laptop. The kitchen is, on a square metre basis, the most expensive in the house to build, with a set of kitchen units costing anything from £2,000 up to £80,000. Although you won't need to choose your exact units early on in the process, you will need to decide on an approximate layout for the sink, cooker and other 'serviced' appliances ready for the first fix stage, and as such most designers will include a rough layout in their original floorplan schemes.

Effective landscaping is essential to help your new home look settled into its plot

Lighting needs to be a key part of the design process

## LANDSCAPING

The work carried out to the rest of your property outside the house. Your initial design for planning application purposes should include a landscaping scheme for two reasons: firstly, it helps show how the new house will bed into its surroundings; and secondly, submitting the scheme as part of the planning application enables you to claim back VAT on the vast majority of the labour and materials you include (such as driveways, walls, fencing, lawn and so on).

A landscape design should provide several different levels of utility for the homeowner: a hard landscaped area around the house to enable sitting and eating outside; driveways and paths to facilitate getting around the plot; and a more decorative area for enjoyment.

You should budget at least £10,000 for landscaping and ensure that it becomes part of your work schedule rather than being left to the end of the project: having the digger on site for the groundworks is a great chance to use it to move around some soil and shape the land the way you want it; additionally, working on it at the same time as the rest of the house means that all the plants and trees you use will have an extra growing season, meaning that the garden looks a little more mature when you move in.

## LIGHTING

Lighting schemes are far removed from the conventional arrangement in traditional homes of a central pendant light in each room augmented by a series of table and floor lamps. A modern lighting circuit should use the full range of available lighting and be complemented by an array of controls — it really can influence how the home is enjoyed.

Task lighting: Lighting for a specific job, such as reading or working in the kitchen. These would usually be lamps or under-cupboard lighting in kitchens to illuminate worktops.

Ambient lighting: Lighting to replace daylight. It usually comes from overhead and can take the form of pendant lighting, spots or downlighters.

Accent lighting: The area of lighting design that has grown in popularity in recent years, it gives texture and depth to corners, walls and features. It might be an uplight to highlight a fireplace, or downlights to give extra appeal to paintings. It should be soft and subtle.

It's not just in design that lighting has enjoyed such phenomenal change in recent years. It's now a requirement under the Building Regulations for some of your lighting to come from energy-efficient bulbs, and in houses that have so many spots and downlights, energy consumption is an important issue. Low-voltage halogen schemes are worth considering as are alternatives such as LEDs (note that low-voltage models will require a transformer).

Finally, controls have developed enormously. 'Mood lighting' is increasingly being specified by self-builders and renovators, particularly at the middle and top ends of the

Traditional oak framing techniques have enjoyed a huge revival with self-builders over the last decade

market, and enable homeowners to co-ordinate their various lighting schemes together with the flick of one switch — no more arrays of dimmer lighting.

## LINTELS

A load-bearing horizontal block that is placed over an entranceway. May be steel, timber or concrete.

## MAIN CONTRACTOR

A professional who organises a construction schedule. A main contractor is the company or person within that company who a self-builder might employ to run a building project. A main contractor would have a wide contacts book of local tradesmen (who would be subcontractors to you) and organise them, and perhaps the materials, for a building project. For this organisational role they would be paid a fee, which commonly they would take as a percentage charge on any labour and materials they supply to you. They might also be known more simply as 'builders'.

## OAK FRAME

The method of building most popular in Tudor times has undergone a remarkable revival in the past 15 years thanks primarily to the efforts of just three package suppliers of oak frame homes to the self-build industry, namely Border Oak, TJ Crump Oakwrights and Carpenter Oak. While this is undoubtedly not a cheap way to build – budget around £1,200-1,500/m2 at least – its popularity lies in the natural beauty of an exposed frame and the special character oak houses possess.

Oak frames are mostly associated with traditional designs but a growing number of contemporary self-builders like to use them as it's relatively straightforward to incorporate large expanses of glazing in the frame designs and the mixture of oak and glass is pleasing to the eye.

Oak frames are erected on site in traditional ways using ancient joining techniques but are also beginning to be combined with modern sheathing systems such as structural insulated panels (SIPs) to combine the benefits of aged beauty with modern insulated walls.

## OFF MAINS

If your plot or house is situated outside a town or city, or is in a small hamlet or village, it's highly possible that it would be classed as being in some way off the mains systems. Although it's highly unlikely to not be connected up to the National Grid for electricity, it is distinctly plausible that it will not be on the gas network and perhaps likely that it won't connect to the mains drainage system. In any of these cases, solutions are easily found and should provide no major additional expense to the self-builder or renovator.

If you're unable to connect to a gas supply, one solution is to opt for LPG — liquid petroleum gas. To install a new LPG tank, it costs around £300 (you'll also need to talk to the planners about this installation). The other common solution is oil — a tank will cost from £200. Local communities will be well served by all the main suppliers of both fuels.

An alternative if you're off mains is to consider one of the renewable sources, such as ground-source heat pumps, solar, wind or even hydro power. They rarely compete economically with gas but are well worth considering as a hedge against rising oil prices in particular.

Off-mains drainage systems offer a similar situation in terms of a mix between established solutions and natural alternatives.

## PACKAGE COMPANIES

Companies operating in the self-build sector who provide a one-stop-shop solution for those looking to build their own home. A package company would provide a design (usually an amendment of an existing standard scheme), provide assistance through the planning and building regulations processes, either provide labour to build the shell of the house or help in finding suitable builders, and even complete all the internal finishes.

In return for their services, package companies would be expected to charge a fee, usually in the form of a percentage addition to all labour and materials (in the same way that a main contractor would), but for many self-builders the benefits of having an experienced ally coupled with a single point of contact more than offsets any additional expenditure. Many package companies offer a fully flexible service where the involvement of the self-builder can be as minimal or as significant as required. Most package companies require payment in stages along the way and when significant deposits are required (particularly the case with timber frame companies) the money should be paid into a third-party 'trust' account to limit its exposure.

While the vast majority of package companies specialise in the timber frame market – and have been behind the boost in popularity of this form of construction – there is a specialist masonry package supplier too.

## PLANNING PERMISSION

In order to build a new dwelling or make significant alterations to an existing dwelling you'll need to gain planning approval, a process which is designed to control development and ensure any new development has a positive contribution to the local area.

The most common application type is for 'Full Planning Permission'. This would cover everything from a new dwelling to an extension. This type of application requires a lot of detail to be submitted from the outset.

An 'Outline Planning Permission' application breaks a submission down into five key sections: layout, scale, appearance, access and landscaping. All or a number of these criteria can be reserved for future consideration. However, detailed supporting information is also needed. The benefits of submitting an Outline Planning application have diminished considerably, as although you do not need detailed drawings for the proposed building, you do need to demonstrate that your proposal withstands the scrutiny of the relevant planning policies. The cost differential isn't great between either type of application, so many experts suggest biting the bullet and going for a 'Full' application from the off.

Listed building applications are needed for any alterations that are made internally or externally to a listed building. My advice with listed buildings is to talk to the local authority, as even minor works may often need listed building consent. The penalties for carrying out unauthorised works to a listed building are severe, with a maximum fine of £20,000, and you could even end up with a criminal record.

Planning applications should be decided within eight weeks although the council can take longer to make a decision if it writes to you within that time period and explains the situation.

## PLASTERBOARD

**See Dry Lining**

## PLOT

The parcel of land on which building might occur. A plot without a viable chance of being built upon is simply land. Hence when looking for plots, you should always check that the piece of land you are looking at has planning permission

currently in place.
Visit www.plotfinder.net

## PROJECT MANAGEMENT

The art of running a self-build or renovation construction project. Project management involves co-ordinating all the trades to ensure that they are on site at the right time, and ensuring that all materials turn up when required. Self-builders who take on the role of project manager can enjoy significant savings on the cost of their new home as opposed to self-builders who employ project managers or main contractors. The term is closely related to that of 'main contractor' although the difference tends to be that project managers often work independently of building firms (they are principally organisers) while main contractors tend to own their own building firms, and often get involved on site with their specific building skills.

Self-builders considering taking on the role of project manager should weigh up the advantages against the disadvantages. The key benefits, in addition to the saving of the project manager's 10-20% fees, are a closer involvement with the project and the ability to ensure that every single element of the home has been specified without outside interference; the downsides are a massively increased workload and stress levels — project managers need to be on site at least twice a day and be able to co-ordinate materials and labour by being seemingly constantly on the phone. It is not particularly advisable for someone running a full-time job to consider project managing a construction project.

Houses can be prefabricated – built in a factory and delivered to site almost completed. It cuts down on build times, but involves making a lot of decisions very early on

## PREFABRICATION

Though the first examples appeared as early as the 1920s, prefabricated homes – constructed primarily off site – first came to prominence in the UK in the 1940s when they were identified as a means of quickly and cheaply providing housing after the War. Whole estates of prefab homes were constructed and by the late 1940s around 150,000 had been built. They were simply laid out, typically consisting of four panels (consisting of steel, aluminium or even asbestos) which could be finished on site to provide living accommodation as well as two bedrooms and an inside bathroom, which made them quite desirable at the time.

They were only designed with a ten-year lifespan but many prefabs still exist today, although in order to comply with the Government's Decent Homes Standard, which is due to come into effect in 2010, many are now being demolished.

There remains a lasting affection for the prefab amongst the UK population and in recent years the traditional-looking prefab has seen itself reborn – at least in principle – both as a concept for progressive architects and, more relevantly to self-builders, a route to a fast and reliable construction time. All of the leading timber frame companies, for instance, rely on prefabrication to some degree in order to minimise time on site.

## QUOTES

A tendered price from a tradesman for a job on site. Assuming that the finished job matches the specification of the job as outlined to the tradesman, this is the price you will pay for the work. It's different to an estimate, which is purely a rough figure from a tradesman for a job.

## RADIATORS

Radiators have been with us for over 100 years and despite the growing number of new self-builds with underfloor heating, they remain the most popular form of heat emitter. Radiators have their drawbacks — their location can often restrict the positioning of furniture in a room, they tend to emit heat unevenly, creating warm and cold spots and, because they convect heat rather than radiate it, they tend to cause draughts. In their favour, however, they are cheap, easy to get hold of, simple to install, convenient for drying clothes and towels and are easily controlled.

## RESTRICTIVE COVENANTS

A covenant (known as a 'burden' in Scotland) is a clause written into a property's title deeds that places controls on how the land is to be used. It is usually put in the deeds by the previous owner of the plot. A typical example of a covenant of this sort is where a homeowner has sold their garden off and has inserted a covenant in the title deeds to prohibit any building on that garden being greater than a single storey, or for windows to face into their house. It might also make allowance for the clawing back of a certain percentage in the uplift of the plot's value if it gains permission for another dwelling, for instance.

Restrictive covenants can be lifted through a lengthy legal process which involves appealing to the Lands Tribunal (this is an option particularly used if the new landowner considers the covenant unfair). If the beneficiary of the covenant is untraceable, it is possible to arrange indemnity cover against anyone claiming rights in the future under the covenant.

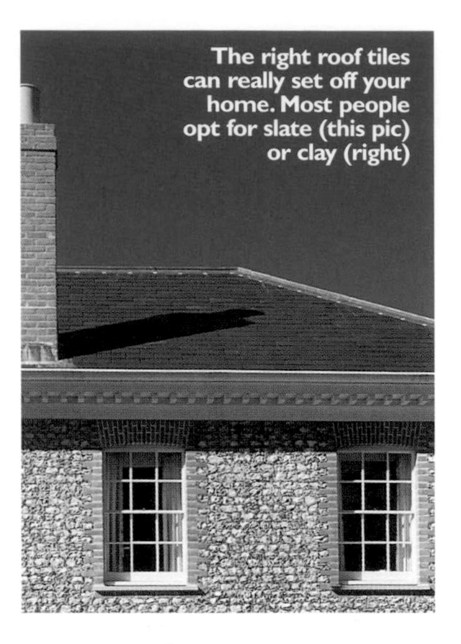

**The right roof tiles can really set off your home. Most people opt for slate (this pic) or clay (right)**

## ROOF TILES

The most popular tiles are small format — known as plain tiles. Measuring 265 x 165mm as standard, they are available in both concrete and clay. At the top end of the plain tile market sit handmade clay tiles. Because of their irregular, individual quality, they have the most character and will lend instant warmth and charm to a new building or help an extension to blend in. They will weather and mellow over time, yet never fade; but, sadly, they are the most expensive choice. A less costly option is to use machine-made clay tiles which are designed to look like handmades, though there are more uniform machine-mades available. There are many suppliers offering a variety of colours, with some producing 'ready-aged' tiles.

Plain concrete tiles are also available, which mimic the appearance of clay. Though they do not hold their looks as well as clay, a good quality tile coloured throughout can be reasonably attractive. At the cheap end of the market are concrete large-format interlocking tiles. Often measuring 330 x 270mm, the size of six plain tiles, they are much quicker to lay — cutting down on labour costs. However, they only work on simple roof designs.

Aside from buying the tiles themselves, a large expense goes towards the cost of laying them.

Second fix for electrics would see swiches put in place

It actually doesn't make much difference in terms of labour whether they are made of clay or concrete if they are the same size and laid using the same method – around £17/hr labour – but large-format interlocking tiles are quite a bit cheaper to lay at around £10/hr.

Tiles can be priced by the thousand, sometimes individually, or by metre square laid. Expect to pay around £750/1,000 for handmade tiles, making a total laid cost of £77/m².Machine-made clay tiles will cost around £300/1,000, so £42/m² laid; plain concrete tiles around £240/1,000, so £38/m² laid; and concrete interlocking around £550/1,000, meaning a laid cost of just £21/m².

This price difference might not sound like much on a m² basis, but has a huge impact over the cost of the whole roof. For example, 100m² of roof covered in handmades will cost around £7,700, whereas the same roof in machine-made clay tiles would cost around £4,200.

Most self-builders will have to seek approval on their choice of roof tile from the planners, to ensure it fits in with the local vernacular.

## SAP RATING

A Standard Assessment Procedure (SAP) rating is the Government's standard system for home energy rating. It estimates the space and hot water heating costs per square metre of floor space and converts it into a rating from 1 to 100, with higher scores (up to 120) being possible with the use of microgeneration to export energy back to the National Grid. SAP assessments are carried out by SAP assessors (they can be done from your building drawings) and a SAP rating is required as part of the Building Regulations. The higher the number, the lower the energy consumption.

A SAP Rating will form part of the Energy Performance Certificate (EPC) which is required on all newly built homes from April 2008. Other parts of the EPC include an Environmental Impact Assessment.

## SCREED

Floor screeding – the laying of the cement floor layer above the floor insulation and below the floor finish (as opposed to using a suspended timber floor) – is a surprisingly complicated area. Screed was traditionally mixed on site and is usually a job for either the plasterers or a specialist floor screeding firm. As a general guide you should expect a floor screed to take around 30mins/m2 to lay, meaning a 100m2 floor area can be screeded in about six man-days. The overall time taken is also affected by whether it is a large space or lots of small rooms. Large spaces are quicker to lay but, as your plasterer will point out, they are not without their problems, especially if you are laying underfloor heating in the screed. BS EN 1264 recommends that you limit the area to be screeded to 40m2, or 8m lengths in any one direction. If you exceed this, you should separate the floor into bays divided by some flexible expansion material. You can generally stop cracking by using mesh or adding fibres to the mix but on very large areas you may find that the screed has a tendency to lift up due to expansion.

In terms of cost, expect to pay in the region of £15/m² including labour and materials.

Screeding is a critical path job and you'll need to plan it into your schedules carefully. Setting time for standard screeds is two days, although fast-set mixes now claim to be set in less than 12 hours — meaning it's best to try and get it done on a Friday to set over the weekend. It's also worth considering drying times — Tarmac's Truscreed mix claims to dry at a rate of 25mm a week (which is fast by comparison to standard mixes), meaning that most applications (65mm or so) will take up to three weeks to dry out properly.

## SECOND FIX

All the work after the plastering to a finished house. Electrical fixtures are

connected to the cables, plumbing pipes are connected up to basins, and so on. Second fix joinery would refer to the fitting of doors (as opposed to door linings, which would be part of the pre-plastering jobs).

## SIPS (STRUCTURAL INSULATED PANELS)

SIPs building is sometimes referred to as timber frame without the timber. Like panelised timber frame, it works on the idea of building up wall and roof panels on flat surfaces and then hoisting them into position, in contrast with masonry build systems which build walls up in situ. Where SIPs differ from timber frame is that they gain their strength not from any timber skeleton but from the rigidity of the panels themselves. The SIPs panels are essentially a sandwich: the filling is a solid thickness insulation, and the bread is made of rigid building boards such as plywood or orientated strand board (OSB). These layers are bonded together which has the effect of making the panels extremely robust. In many ways, the technique is similar to how aircraft wings are designed, with two skins wrapped around a lightweight core and then welded together to form a single element.

Slopes may add to the difficulty (and cost) of building, but they can be responsible for highly innovative design schemes too

SIPs panels consist of insulation sandwiched between two sheets of OSB

The advantages are that you create a structure with superb insulation levels, few cold bridges and excellent airtightness levels. Plus, in the right hands, SIPs have the potential for faster construction speeds than timber frame. The panelised roof elements lend themselves to building rooms in the roof, in a simpler and quicker manner than traditional methods.

## SLOPES

A sloping site is both a problem and a gift. The problem: it adds complexity and, therefore, cost to the project. The gift: when you've finished, you'll have a much more interesting house — possibly with a great view. Of course, it all depends on the slope. It may be that you don't even realise you have a slope until you get the laser levels out and start surveying; on the other hand, if you go and buy a cliff, it will not come as a great surprise to find out that at least half your build budget will be eaten up by the ensuing civil engineering works. Typically, you might expect a 1 in 10 slope – about 6° – on a modest building plot to add a figure of around £10,000 to the overall costs.

## SNAGGING

The list of jobs that need finishing off at the end of a building contract. These usually consist of joining-up jobs or dealing with niggling cracks, perhaps. Getting a builder to come back to deal with these jobs is often quite difficult and it's wise to try and leave some money in the contract to encourage him to deal with the snags.

## STAIRCASES

If windows are the most important external features of a house, then staircases are probably the most important internal ones. In terms

An entirely glass staircase

Tension wires act as balusters on this modern staircase

This modern staircase looks almost skeletal, with timber treads on a steel frame

of exactness and line, constructing staircases poses problems as difficult as those of making complicated pieces of furniture, while calculating the space and headroom required for the staircase is one of the greatest challenges to any self-builder. It is all a question of style and subtlety — and it may mean a long search for a joiner you consider capable of the job.

## STAIRCASE TERMS EXPLAINED:

**The Going and the Rising:** The going is the length of the flight from the first riser to the trim at the top. The rising is the height from the floor to the trim.

**Tread and Riser:** Each step usually comprises two parts: the tread, which is the section you step onto, and the riser, which is the vertical section beneath. An open-tread staircase has no risers.

**Winders and Kites:** Wedge and kite-shaped treads that enable a staircase to rise as it turns. Used in place of a quarter landing they reduce the going of a staircase. Ideal for tight spaces.

**A Winding Staircase:** A stair that rises by the use of straight flights connected by winders and kites in place of landings.

**Nosing:** The outer edge of the tread which projects beyond the outer face of the riser. In a traditional wooden stair it is usually rounded, chamfered or moulded.

**The Strings:** The two sloping members that carry the ends of the treads and in the case of a timber stair, hold it all together. An open-string or cut-string staircase, which follows the line of the treads, has a totally different look from a closed-string staircase. A cut string follows the line of the treads and risers while a closed string is straight, following the angle of the stair with the treads and risers housed into it.

**Balusters:** The wooden posts, usually turned, that support the handrails. Sometimes people refer to these as banisters but the correct architectural term is baluster. The whole assembly is called a balustrade.

**Newel Posts:** The posts at the ends of flights which transfer the weight of the stair to the floor and support the balustrades.

**Cantilevered Treads:** A staircase with no external bracing — i.e. it appears to be self-supporting.

**Flying Stair:** A flight cantilevered from the stairwell without a newel.

**Geometric Stair:** A flying stair with an inner edge that forms a continuous curve.

**Helical Stair:** The correct name for a spiral stair.

**Volute:** A spiral scroll turned in solid timber that forms the stop at the bottom of a hand rail, usually ornate in style and connected to a cluster of spindles.

## STONE

Stone for building comes in three

Stone can be used in modern settings as well as more traditional

distinct types: natural, rubble and reconstituted. Each is capable of giving your project that authentic rustic look. Natural stone is blasted, dug and generally extracted from a quarry. For ease of building, dressed stone (faced up after quarrying into convenient shapes for building) is the best bet. If you plan to build a block inner wall and use the stone to form the face, the stone will have to be at least 100mm thick to comply with Building Regulations.

Rubble walls are made up of random-sized pieces of natural stone set into mortar. They need an outer wall to fix to — so you must factor in that extra depth of blocks and the associated labour when estimating costs (£18-20/$m^2$).

Material-wise, dressed natural stone is very expensive to buy at around £40/$m^2$ and you won't get much change from £80 to get someone to lay a square metre for you. Rubble stone can be had for as little as £10/$m^2$ but it's slower to lay than dressed stone so expect to pay at least £100/$m^2$ for this. Add the £18 20/$m^2$ for extra blockwork and rubble walls start looking quite expensive.

There are 440 active stone quarries in the UK, so getting stone isn't going to be a problem. The type you end up using is likely to depend on where you live, with different types of stone dominant in different parts of the UK.

## SUBCONTRACTORS

A tradesman who works for your main contractor is, to you, a subcontractor. As the subcontractor (often shortened to 'subbie') is managed by the main contractor rather than you directly, it is usually best to initially address any concerns with any tradesmen to the main contractor on site.

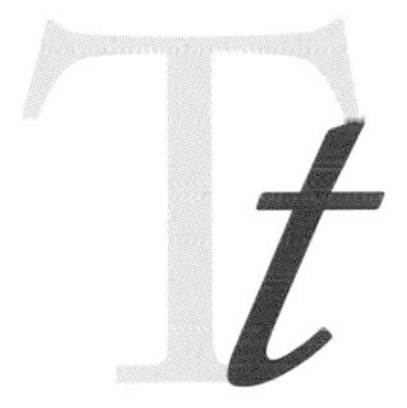

## TIMBER FRAME

As its name implies, timber frame construction is a method of building which relies on a timber frame as a basic means of structural support.

During construction, open-panel timber frame is covered internally by plasterboard, filled with insulation. Moisture/vapour barriers are incorporated and the outer leaf of the wall completes the structure. The outer leaf is typically

Timber frame homes tend to be slightly quicker to build than those built in blockwork

stone, brick, render or timber to suit the local vernacular and planning requirements. As a result it's often hard to tell whether or not it is a timber frame dwelling.

Timber frames account for a significant minority (about 25%) of the English, Northern Irish and Welsh construction markets but enjoy about 70% market share in Scotland. In North America it accounts for some 90% of low-rise buildings.

The key benefits of self-building using timber frames are that they tend to be quicker to erect on site (although this is often offset by longer lead-in times for the frame to be delivered), they are able to accommodate high levels of insulation, and due to its prefabricated nature reduces the potential for errors on site. One of the key disadvantages of timber frame construction is that it cannot accommodate solid first floors, which can mean that sound travels easier around a timber frame house — however, this can easily be overcome with extra levels of acoustic insulation

## U-VALUES

A U-value measures the heat loss through a material — in this case, the roof, external walls and ground floor of a building. A window, for instance, would have a U-value of its own which contributes to the overall U-value of a wall. The lower the U-value, the lower the level of heat loss. U-values are indicated in units of 'watts per metre squared per degree kelvin', or W/m2K. Maximum U-values permissible under the latest Building Regulations are 0.35 for walls and floors and 0.25 for roofs. Windows have a permitted U-value of 1.8. For the first time, changes in the Building Regulations in 2006 specified that where a house is being renovated, if 25% or more of the total surface area is being renovated, then the whole 'element' (or house) will need to comply with U-value requirements.

## UNDERFLOOR HEATING

A great many self-builders plump for underfloor heating (UFH) instead of radiators. Here, you bury plastic pipework within the cement screed or under a timber floor, and you use the whole floor as a radiator. It's a little more expensive to install but it's proved very popular with self-builders over the years because: the heat radiates slowly upwards (it is, therefore, reckoned to be much more pleasant); there are no hot spots or drafts; there are no unsightly radiators; there are energy-efficiency benefits as UFH operates at low temperatures.

The downside tends to be that UFH is far less controllable than radiator-based heating systems, so much so that many people leave UFH on 24/7, although with sophisticated controls it is possible to manage two or three temperature regimes. They can take a long time to get a house warm and, having

Underfloor heating requires lower hot water temperatures, making it more efficient than radiator systems

got warm, they take an equally long time to cool down, which can cause overheating. UFH, therefore, tends to suit houses in constant occupation, rather than those where everyone is out all day. One frequent compromise is to fit UFH on the ground floor and radiators upstairs.

There are several issues to be aware of with UFH. The pipes are laid out around the house in separate loops. This way there are no joints below ground. Each loop, or zone, is brought back to a manifold, usually one per floor, which is usually where the controls are located. You can control the individual loops, just as you can control radiators, but if a loop covers two or more rooms, then you have no way of controlling what goes on in each room. More critically, the heat output from UFH varies according to the floor covering: stone and tile transmit heat easily, wood less so, carpet much less so. Thus it is critical to decide on your floor coverings at the outset so that you can ensure each area corresponds with an UFH zone. If your supplier is on the ball, they will be aware of these issues, but you can't rely on this.

## VAT

**Do I have to pay VAT...**
**For New Build?**
If a self-builder uses a VAT-registered builder to have their new home built on a supply-and-fix basis, no VAT should be charged on any of the work or materials.

If a self-builder employs VAT-registered supply-and-fix tradesmen for any part of the work to their new home, then the contract will not attract VAT. Materials purchased by the self-builder will attract VAT at the standard rate of 20% — but most of this can be recovered at the end of the project.

**For Conversions?**
A supply-and-fix builder must charge VAT at the rate of 5% on the full contract value. Labour-only and supply-and-fix contracts with VAT-registered subcontractors will also be subject to VAT at 5%. Material purchases by the converter attract VAT at 20%. Most of the VAT paid for labour and materials is recovered at the end of the project.

**For Renovations and Extensions?**
Those turning an existing dwelling into a better one will have to pay VAT at the full rate of 20% on top of the price for labour and materials, with no facility to reclaim it. But, if the property has been unoccupied for 10 years or more, it is treated like a 'conversion' and the VAT rules are as detailed above. There is a concession whereby if a dwelling has been unoccupied for more than two years, a VAT-registered builder can charge VAT at a rate of 5%.

Warranties form an essential guarantee for you and future buyers

## VENTILATION

The Building Regulations demand that every new home must have a ventilation strategy, over and above just leaving the windows open. What they are trying to achieve is to have a constant flow of fresh air coming through the house so that the internal air changes once every two hours. This is reckoned to be ideal for controlling humidity levels and keeping air quality good. The regulations also require that the so-called 'wet rooms' – bathrooms, kitchen, utility area – have suitable extract arrangements to help dissipate smells and high-humidity air.

The best-known, and most expensive, alternative strategy is a whole-house ventilation solution, as widely adopted in Sweden and Canada. Fresh air is drawn in and piped around the house into the 'dry rooms' (living rooms, bedrooms) and stale air is extracted from the wet rooms.

## WARRANTIES

A warranty is a form of guarantee on a property. While it is not mandatory, the requirement for a warranty is usually enforced by mortgage providers who see it as an essential part of a home's value. Warranties will be requested by a vendor's solicitor so if you intend to sell your new home on within 10 years (the standard warranty period) it is worth getting one. You'll need to contact one of the

Weatherboarding can give new buildings a more tradition look

providers at plans stage and warranties are enforced by regular inspection visits. They cost around 1% of your build cost and are provided by a number of private companies, the most popular of which is the NHBC.

## WEATHER-BOARDING

Timber facings can be seen on houses up and down the country, with particular strongholds in East Anglia and Kent. Since the 1980s, rural England has been awash with the whiff of cut timber and creosote, thanks to all the barn conversions and their freshly replaced facings. Timber facings are usually attached horizontally to battens running vertically up an outer skin of blockwork. Sometimes, they are attached vertically, which works well with curved surfaces, or diagonally, for a chevron finish. The most common types of boards for timber facing are sawn featheredge and planed shiplap. Featheredged boards usually overlap one another to form a fence-like weatherproof surface. Shiplap, on the other hand, forms a neat, flush surface and is joined together either by tongue-and-groove or a sturdy rebate.

## ZERO-CARBON HOMES

A zero carbon home is one that produces more energy than it uses over the course of a year, although the exact definitions are still up for debate. The key principles of a zero carbon home are high levels of insulation, airtightness and low energy requirements in electricity, coupled with renewable on-site power generation. According to Government targets all homes in England and Scotland will have to be zero carbon by 2016; in Wales by 2013.

Zero carbon homes, such as this from Kingpsan Potton, produce as much or more energy than they consume over a year